Kodiak Bears &
the *Exxon Valdez*

KODIAK BEARS & THE *EXXON VALDEZ*

Edited by
Tim Richardson and Dave Cline

A KODIAK BROWN BEAR TRUST BOOK

Cover photo credits:
Kodiak bear inset, by HowieGarber/wanderlustimages.com
Exxon Valdez tanker in Prince William Sound,
Anchorage Daily News by Erik Hill

Cover and book design by Sims Design Co. LLC, Washington, D.C.

Printed by A&T Publishing and Printing, Inc., Anchorage, AK

This book is printed on recycled paper.

ISBN: 0-9706021-0-3

Kodiak Bears & the Exxon Valdez is dedicated to the many conservation minded Americans who, by taking a stand, are helping ensure that the majestic Kodiak brown bear and its wilderness haunts in Alaska's Kodiak Archipelago remain a part of the American experience.

The kings of England formerly had their forests to hold the king's game, for sport or food, sometimes destroying villages to create and extend them. . . . Why should not we, who have renounced the king's authority, have our national preserves, where no villages need be destroyed, in which the bear . . . may still exist . . . or shall we, like villains, grub them all up, poaching on our own national domain?

HENRY DAVID THOREAU
From *The Journals*

CONTENTS

Acknowledgments XI
List of Abbreviations XVI
List of Maps XVII
Preface XVIII

INTRODUCTION   Tim Richardson   **3**

CHAPTER I.
KODIAK'S OIL SPILL SUMMER   Jay Bellinger   **13**

OIL SPILL PICTORIAL   **39**

CHAPTER 2.
AN ALUTIIQ PERSPECTIVE   Emil Christiansen   **47**

OUR ANGER HAS NOWHERE TO GO   Dolly Reft   **70**

CHAPTER 3.
THE MAJESTIC KODIAK BROWN BEAR
Victor G. Barnes, Jr.   **75**

CHAPTER 4.
RIVERS OF SALMON, VALLEYS OF BEARS
Dave Cline   **91**

CHAPTER 5.
AT HOME IN THE AFOGNAK WILDERNESS
Colleen Rankin   **113**

CHAPTER 6.

IN THE FOOTPRINTS OF THE GREAT BEAR
Scott Stouder **129**

EPILOGUE   Douglas H. Grann **153**

Addendum **164**
  Exhibit 1 Executive Order 8857 **165**
  Exhibit 2 Terms of the *Exxon Valdez* settlement **166**
  Exhibit 3 Organizational Structure of *Exxon Valdez*
      Oil Spill Trustee Council **167**
  Exhibit 4 Habitat Protection and Acquisition **168**
  Exhibit 5 *Exxon Valdez* Impact on Marine Birds **169**
  Exhibit 6 Value to Fishermen of Statewide Salmon **170**
For More Information **171**

ACKNOWLEDGMENTS

Kodiak Bears & the Exxon Valdez is a collaborative book by seven authors describing the nation's worst environmental accident and a large-scale habitat conservation effort that sprang from its aftermath. The Kodiak Archipelago habitat conservation agreements and continuing opportunities described by the authors occur in the context of the Exxon Valdez Oil Spill Restoration Plan and reflect America's growing desire for abundant fish and wildlife resources, intact wild landscapes, and healthy marine ecosystems.

The oil spill restoration plan was an unprecedented exercise in environmental mitigation. The plan was designed and implemented by a six member state and federal trustee council which oversaw the oil spill damage assessment, provided for public input, and allocated the $1 billion Exxon settlement ($900 million civil, $100 million criminal) approved by U.S. District Court Judge H. Russel Holland.

The political climate shaping *Exxon Valdez* restoration was marked by aroused public emotions, stark polarization between the state and federal governments, and determined competition among oil spill victims and others, who were potential recipients of millions of dollars of government largesse.

To an objective observer in the early 1990s, the prospects for oil spill impacted fish and wildlife and the public becoming primary beneficiaries of the Exxon settlement were a matter of reasonable doubt. The likelihood of boondoggles, indecision, and the squandering of resources was far higher.

Nonetheless, as *Kodiak Bears & the Exxon Valdez* argues, the *Exxon Valdez* Oil Spill Restoration Plan is a runaway success for the environment and people, including the economy of the region. The habitat conservation successes in the Kodiak Archipelago are mirrored by similar spectacular achievements in Prince William Sound and on the Kenai Peninsula, which taken together received the lion's share of the Exxon fine. In addition to habitat protection, the final oil spill restoration plan made sizeable investments in marine research and in an endowment fund that should provide base line understanding of the ecology of the Gulf of Alaska, along with the financial resources to allow future policymakers to make informed decisions.

The *Exxon Valdez* Oil Spill Trustee Council (EVOS Trustee Council) deserves great credit for the positive results from the Exxon settlement, including the habitat conservation successes in the Kodiak Archipelago. The council members who forged the consensus for adopting the oil spill restoration plan were Charlie Cole, Alaska Department of Law; Carl Rosier, Alaska Department of Fish and Game; John Sandor, Alaska Department of Environmental Conservation; George Frampton, U.S. Department of Interior; Douglas Hall, National Oceanic and Atmospheric Administration; and Michael Barton, U.S. Forest Service.

Subsequent members of the EVOS Trustee Council who made vital decisions to further habitat protection are Bruce Botello, Michelle Brown, Terry Garcia, Dave Gibbons, Marilyn Heiman, Phil Janik, Jim Lyons, Steve Pennoyer, Frank Rue, Craig Tillery, Deborah Williams, and Jim Wolfe.

Trustee Council executive directors Jim Ayers and Molly McCammon displayed great skill and patience in achieving stakeholder buy-in to the restoration plan and in balancing the often competing interests among state and federal agencies.

The Bush administration, including Interior Secretary Manuel Lujan, helped achieve the largest environmental fine in U.S. history and successfully urged that the $1 billion Exxon settlement be spent in the oil spill region instead of being deposited in the Alaska or federal treasuries.

The Clinton administration, and above all Interior Secretary Bruce Babbitt, was decisive in making sure that habitat protection was prioritized in the EVOS restoration plan. Secretary Babbitt deserves special recognition for assuring the Kodiak National Wildlife Refuge (Kodiak NWR) conservation successes. Council on Environmental Quality chair Kathleen McGinty, Bureau of Indian Affairs assistant secretary Ada Deer, and White House Office of Intergovernmental Affairs liaison Loretta Avent played important roles in the administration's support of habitat protection and Native Alaskan outreach.

Alaska Governor Walter Hickel insisted that the oil spill settlement be no less than $1 billion (equal to 20 percent of Exxon's 1989 profits). Equally important, Hickel and his Attorney General Charlie Cole developed a working relationship with Bruce Babbitt and George Frampton in the EVOS arena that transcended the sharp differences common in most other Alaska-federal issues. Alaska Governor Tony Knowles continued the state's emphasis on habitat conservation, extolling intact ecosystems as another "permanent fund" for Alaska's economy.

U.S. Senator Ted Stevens worked with Congressman Don Young to obtain the first actual funding for the Kodiak NWR habitat conservation efforts by shepherding Land and Water Conservation Fund dollars through the U.S. Congress.

U.S. Fish and Wildlife Service (USFWS) directors John Turner, Mollie Beattie, Jamie Clark, and acting director John Rogers were effective champions for the Kodiak NWR. USFWS regional directors Walt Stieglitz and Dave Allen, plus Department of Interior and USFWS personnel Don Barry, Dan Sakura, Glenn Elison, Karen Kovacs, Phil Million, Bruce Batten, Steve Shuck, Gary Muehlenhardt, and Christine Mullaney played important roles in Kodiak Archipelago habitat protection. Alaska Department of Natural Resources deputy commissioner Marty Rutherford and EVOS Trustee Council staff Eric Myers, Art Weiner, and Mark Broderson and others were invaluable sources of information and encouragement.

None of the Kodiak Archipelago conservation successes would have been possible without the willingness of Kodiak and Afognak Native corporations to participate in *Exxon Valdez* restoration. Conservationists owe a debt of gratitude to native corporation shareholders and board members and Afognak Native Corporation President Ole Olsen; Akhiok Kaguyak, Inc. President Ralph Eluska; Koniag, Inc. President Dennis Metrokin and CEO Uwe Gross; and Old Harbor Native Corporation President Emil Christiansen, for their sustained leadership in a multi-year project.

Negotiators for both sides of the land transactions exhibited determination and uncommon creativity to reach the "win-win" result described in *Kodiak Bears & the Exxon Valdez*. On the landowners' side of the table were Walt Ebell, Roy Jones, Larry Landry, Tim Mahoney, Bill Timme, and Jim Wilkens. The federal negotiators were Curtis 'Buff' Bohlen, Barry Roth, and Bob Putz (on loan from The Conservation Fund).

The State of Alaska negotiators were Department of Law attorneys Alex Swiderski and Craig Tillery.

Kodiak Island Borough Mayor Jerome Selby was an especially effective advocate for Kodiak's people and natural resources in EVOS restoration.

Numerous organizations lent support to Kodiak and Afognak habitat protection, including the Alaska Center for the Environment, Alaska Conservation Foundation, Alaska Rainforest Campaign, American Conservation Association, American Land Conservancy, American Sportfishing Association, American Rivers, Boone & Crockett Club, Camp Fire Conservation Fund, Congressional Sportsmen's Caucus, The Conservation Fund, Dallas Ecological Foundation, Dallas Safari Club, Federation of Fly Fishermen, Great Bear Foundation, International Association of Bear Research and Management, Izaak Walton League, Kodiak Island Sportsmen's Association, Mule Deer Foundation, National Audubon Society, National Fish & Wildlife Foundation, National Geographic Society, National Rifle Association, National Wildlife Federation, National Wildlife Refuge Association, Natural Resources Defense Council, Nature Conservancy of Alaska, New York State Conservation Council, North America Hunting Club, Oregon Hunters Association, Pacific Seabird Group, Rocky Mountain Elk Foundation, Safari Club International, Sierra Club, Smithsonian Institution, Trust for Public Land, Vital Ground, Wilderness Society, Wildlife Conservation Society, Wildlife Forever, Wildlife Legislative Fund of America, Wildlife Management Institute, and World Wildlife Fund.

Special thanks for the publication of *Kodiak Bears & the Exxon Valdez* go to John Grassy of Avocet Communications for copy-editing, Kathleen Sims for book design and layout, Christine Hauser for proof-reading and photo research, the *Kodiak Daily Mirror* for donating use of photos from the summer of 1989, and Len Kimball for *Mirror* photo selection. Joe Hunt, director of media relations for the EVOS Trustee Council provided oil spill related maps plus photos by Roy Corral and Daniel Zatz.

Kodiak Brown Bear Trust trustees Daniel Beardsley, Jay Bellinger, Dave Cline, and John Merrick deserve thanks for their enthusiastic support of *Kodiak Bears & the Exxon Valdez* and their steady guidance to the Trust. Support from the Pew Fellowship in Marine Conservation enabled Trust Chairman Dave Cline to participate in the oil spill restoration effort.

FINANCIAL SUPPORT

Financial support for the Kodiak Brown Bear Trust's publication of *Kodiak Bears & the Exxon Valdez* was provided by the following organizations: Wildlife Forever contributed a grant that matched donations from the Alaska Conservation Foundation, American Conservation Association, Camp Fire Conservation Fund, Conservation Force, The Conservation Fund, Dallas Ecological Foundation, National Rifle Association, National Wildlife Refuge Association, Rocky Mountain Elk Foundation, and Wildlife Management Institute.

Safari Club International (SCI) and the following SCI chapters contributed generously to *Kodiak Bears & the Exxon Valdez*:

Alaska	Kansas City
Amarillo	Minnesota
California Central Valley	Montana
California Sierra	National Capital
Central New Jersey	Nebraska
Central Washington	New York Tri State
Chesapeake	Northern Arizona
Connecticut	Orange County
Flint	Pittsburgh
Fox River	Portland
Georgia	San Diego
Golden Gate	Southern Arizona Bow
Golden State Bowhunters	South Texas
Granite Bay	Tampa
Greater Atlanta	West Michigan Bow
Idaho	Wisconsin
James River	

Views expressed in *Kodiak Bears & the Exxon Valdez* are those of each author.

LIST OF ABBREVIATIONS

ADF&G	Alaska Department of Fish & Game
AKI	Akhiok Kaguyak, Inc.
ANCSA	Alaska Native Claims Settlement Act
ANILCA	Alaska National Interest Lands Conservation Act
DOI	Department of Interior
EVOS	*Exxon Valdez* Oil Spill
EVOS Trustee Council	*Exxon Valdez* Oil Spill Trustee Council
Kodiak NWR	Kodiak National Wildlife Refuge
NOAA	National Oceanic and Atmospheric Administration
Mirror	*Kodiak Daily Mirror*
LWCF	Land and Water Conservation Fund
NWR	National Wildlife Refuge
OHNC	Old Harbor Native Corporation
Trust	Kodiak Brown Bear Trust
USFWS	U.S. Fish and Wildlife Service

LIST OF MAPS

Page 4   Land ownership pattern of the Kodiak Archipelago prior to the EVOS Restoration Plan,

Page 23   The geographic spread of the Exxon Valdez oil spill,

Page 27   Oil spill region superimposed off the eastern coast of the United States,

Page 93   Land ownership pattern of the Karluk and Sturgeon river area, state and federal conservation units,

Page 158   EVOS protected habitat and Trust priorities for future protection in the Kodiak Archipelago

PREFACE

Thanks to the vigorous and effective intervention of the National Audubon Society, National Wildlife Federation, and Sierra Club, the Kodiak Brown Bear Trust was established in 1981 to mitigate effects of the Terror Lake Hydroelectric Project on the world renowned Kodiak brown bears and their habitats. The Trust is a non-profit organization based in Anchorage, Alaska, overseen by four trustees and administered by an executive director.

The Trust's mission is:

> "To support conservation of the majestic Kodiak brown bear through habitat protection, research, and public education."

Through close collaboration with its many partners and the EVOS Trustee Council, the Trust has played a key role in helping secure permanent protection to 376,000 acres of prime coastal wildlife habitat in the Kodiak Archipelago. The majority of the acquired lands have been returned to the Kodiak National Wildlife Refuge to make it whole again. This represents the largest addition made to a refuge by purchased acquisitions in the nearly 100 year history of the National Wildlife Refuge System. These collaborative efforts have benefited a diversity of coastal and marine wildlife damaged by the tragic 1989 *Exxon Valdez* oil spill as well as Kodiak brown bears. As we enter a new millennium, and a third decade for the Trust, we and our many allies are committed to helping raise the funds necessary to acquire, or purchase conservation easements for, another 215,000 acres from willing sellers in the archipelago.

There are many important lessons to be learned in the conservation success story being played out in Alaska's spectacularly beautiful Kodiak

Archipelago. These lessons teach us how best to respond when confronted with a human-caused ecological disaster like an oil spill. The first is to hold the guilty party fully responsible for its deeds. Another is to insist that most of the civil and criminal penalties collected are used to restore damaged resources. What we have learned at Kodiak is that when conservation-minded Americans join forces in a common restoration endeavor focused on habitat protection, irreplaceable parts of our nation's natural heritage can be secured for the use and enjoyment of this and future generations. In the process, coastal economies based on use of renewable natural resources receive a more sustainable future.

"By the mid-1980s, Washington had taken stock of the situation, which posed what could be termed a 'lose-lose' scenario. . . . The U.S. Department of Interior targeted Native inholdings in the Kodiak NWR as the number one federal land acquisition priority in Alaska."

—*TIM RICHARDSON*

Events of the magnitude of the Exxon Valdez *disaster exert life-changing influence on the people they touch. For congressional aide Tim Richardson, the oil spill meant a career turn, trading the marble halls and cramped offices of Capitol Hill for the remote shores and Native villages of the Kodiak Archipelago.*

Experience gained in advising candidates or passing legislation got applied to conservation politics, media outreach, and years of meetings seeking consensus among Native corporations, economic stakeholders, refuge user groups, and state and federal officials who would be making far-reaching decisions in spending the $1 billion Exxon fine.

After touring the Kodiak Archipelago for the House Merchant Marine and Fisheries Committee in the year of the oil spill, 1989, Tim left congressional staff life behind and spent five years working for Native landowners. In 1995 he became executive director of the Kodiak Brown Bear Trust and is co-editor of Kodiak Bears & the Exxon Valdez.

President Franklin D. Roosevelt created the Kodiak NWR
by executive order. Photo shows FDR fishing on Kodiak during World War II,
(Kodiak Historical Society).

INTRODUCTION

TIM RICHARDSON

On March 24th, 1989, the *Exxon Valdez* supertanker ran aground in Prince William Sound, delivering eleven million gallons of its cargo into one of the world's most prolific marine and coastal ecosystems. In the weeks and months to follow, the *Exxon Valdez* spill would earn its rightful designation as an environmental catastrophe, the likes of which had never been experienced in the U.S., and rarely in the world.

The story of the devastation spread more rapidly than the wind and tide-dispersed oil—blackened beaches, wildlife mortalities of almost unimaginable proportions, profound social and economic upheaval for the people of the region. There may be hundreds of oil tankers traveling the oceans at any given time, but a decade later, in the minds of most Americans, there is only one supertanker with a name.

The *Exxon Valdez* spill is remembered first and foremost as a disaster, and of the retrospectives to already have appeared, many pay tribute to what was lost and examine the ways in which the natural world has recovered or failed to recover. The essays in *Kodiak Bears & the Exxon Valdez* offer a less-well-known story, one that began after the spill and continues to this day. Set on Alaska's stunning Kodiak Archipelago, these are stories of both tragedy and triumph borne of environmental disaster.

Perched on the rim of the North Pacific, almost due north of the Hawaiian Islands, the Kodiak Archipelago is a mosaic of islands, offshore islets, reefs, and seamounts; its centerpiece is 100-mile-long Kodiak Island, the nation's second-largest island. A remarkably diverse

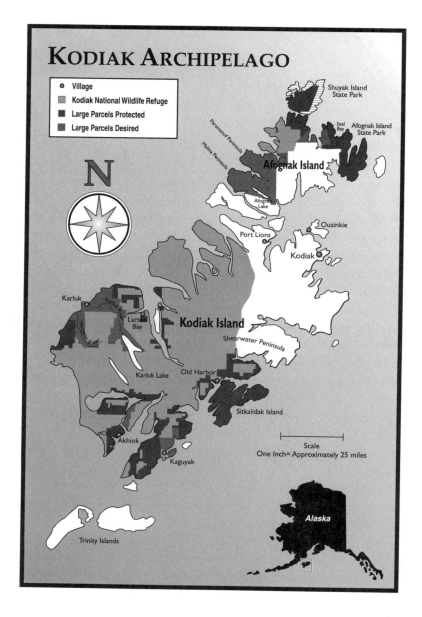

KODIAK ARCHIPELAGO

- ○ Village
- Kodiak National Wildlife Refuge
- Large Parcels Protected
- Large Parcels Desired

Shuyak Island
State Park

Seal Bay   Afognak Island
State Park

Paramanof Peninsula

Malina Peninsula

N

Afognak Island

Afognak Lake

Ouzinkie

Port Lions

Kodiak

Karluk

Karluk River

Larsen Bay

Broken Point River

Kodiak Island

Shearwater Peninsula

Karluk Lake   Old Harbor

Sitkalidak Island

Akhiok

Kaguyak

Scale
One Inch= Approximately 25 miles

Alaska

Trinity Islands

Complex private and public land ownership patterns pose serious threats to brown bear management in the Kodiak Archipelago (map EVOS Trustee Council).

landscape is here—coastlines, rugged mountains, rivers and lakes, wetlands, expansive valleys, and sweeping mountain cirques. The maritime climate is cool, cloudy, wet, the product of Aleutian low fronts and gusting "southeasters," which pump fog, rain, sleet, and violent storms over the land day upon day. Suddenly a northwest wind arrives; the days are sunny, the nights bright with stars. Against a blue sky, the lush landscape appears in endless shades of green, an unforgettable image that has bestowed upon Kodiak its second name: the Emerald Isle.

It would be hard to overstate the ecological wealth of this region. On Afognak Island, second-largest in the archipelago, are old-growth forests of Sitka spruce, rich tidal estuaries, and some of the world's most prolific salmon runs. Wild and remote, Afognak drew the attention of President Benjamin Harrison in 1892 and was designated the Afognak Forest and Fish Culture Reserve, the second Alaskan lands after the Pribolof fur seal sanctuary set aside for conservation. In 1907, President Theodore Roosevelt made Afognak the first unit of the National Forest System in Alaska.

Amidst this union of land and sea, millions of pink, chinook, coho, and chum salmon return each year to their natal rivers—the Karluk, Afognak, Sturgeon, and Ayakulik—on Kodiak and Afognak islands. River otters and red fox hunt along lakes and waterways. Sitka blacktailed deer browse on the mountainsides. Summers bring a host of neotropical migrants, such as the orange-crowned warbler and golden-crowned sparrows, to nesting grounds on heath and tundra shrub. Out in the sea, not far from shore, whales, marine birds, sea lions, and seals pursue their ways of life.

One animal, the Kodiak brown bear, stands above all. This remarkable creature is the product of Kodiak's matrix of climate, landscape diversity, and bountiful salmon runs. A large male bear, fattened in fall for hibernation, may weigh 1,500 pounds, making it the largest land carnivore on earth. During summer salmon runs, Kodiak's rivers host a congregation of brown bears unmatched in the world. Gilbert M. Grosvenor, chairman of the National Geographic Society, has stated that, "Perhaps no creatures on earth inspire greater awe than the majestic bears that roam Alaska's Kodiak Island."

President Benjamin Harrison (standing, right, in duck blind) created the Afognak Forest and Fish Culture Reserve in 1892 (Indiana Historical Society).

A place as vital and wild and unique as Kodiak—a place that evolved a separate race of giant bears—is a world that by today's standards is almost too good to be true. Worlds like this perish; many already have or are well on their way. Though the Kodiak bear might be a giant, the animal and its world are almost painfully fragile.

In 1941, at the urging of conservationists and sportsmen concerned for its wild bears, President Franklin D. Roosevelt designated two-thirds of the island—nearly two million acres—as Kodiak National Wildlife Refuge (Kodiak NWR). In 1971, the refuge and surrounding lands were subject to a new political development. The U.S. Congress passed the Alaska Native Claims Settlement Act (ANCSA), which empowered Kodiak's Native Alutiiq people to make huge land withdrawals from inside the refuge boundaries and to use these lands for economic self-sufficiency. Overnight, some 310,000 acres of the refuge, including several major salmon rivers and coastal lowlands, became private property. In 1980, the Alaska National Interest Lands Conservation Act (ANILCA) conveyed another 390,000 acres elsewhere in the archipelago, including Afognak Island.

ANCSA and ANILCA were efforts to fulfill aboriginal rights agreed to in the 1867 U.S. purchase of Alaska by returning to the Alutiiq people control over lands they had occupied for thousands of years. Last-minute political maneuvering during the ANCSA vote in Congress, however, added a final, fateful twist. Congressman John Dingell of Michigan inserted language in the bill preventing the sale of Native corporation stock to non-Natives for twenty years; guaranteed the federal government the right of first refusal on any sale of land parcels located within the boundaries of Kodiak NWR; stipulated that all ANCSA lands in the Kodiak NWR be managed by USFWS as a wildlife refuge with the intent that Native landowners would not be allowed to develop their holdings in ways deemed "inconsistent with the purpose of the refuge."

Alutiiq leaders were incensed. Under a law meant to avoid the Indian reservation system in Alaska through adoption of the Native corporation model they had been given title to lands they believed would provide important economic opportunities. Instead, lands in the deal had been returned with a series of restrictions dictated by outsiders.

Though the law required that Kodiak brown bears enjoy unrestricted use of rivers and coastal areas, Native lands within Kodiak NWR could be developed in a number of ways. Extensive recreation-based development—hunting and fishing lodges, resorts, airstrips, cabins along rivers and lakes, roads and ATV trails—loomed as the most viable option. Outside refuge boundaries, virtually anything was possible.

By the mid-1980s, Washington had taken stock of the situation, which posed what could be termed a "lose-lose" scenario. From the point of view of conservationists, 700,000 acres of the world's most pristine forests and watersheds were under threat of logging or commercial development. For the Native-formed corporations and their shareholders, development options on Kodiak NWR inholdings were clouded by the requirement that they not interfere with wild Kodiak bears.

The U.S. Department of Interior targeted Native inholdings on Kodiak NWR as the number one federal land aquisition priority in Alaska. The Reagan administration developed a proposal called "Megatrade" to return Kodiak NWR inholdings to public hands and compensate Native landowners. The deal involved potential oil and gas royalties from the Arctic NWR if Congress opened it to drilling, but this highly controversial initiative, opposed by the State of Alaska and environmentalists, stalled in the early months of 1989. On March 24 of that same year came a news alert that would toss all of these cards into the air: the *Exxon Valdez* lay crippled in Prince William Sound . . . .

Without exception, the authors here are collaborators of the Kodiak Brown Bear Trust, a conservation group that would play a pivotal role in picking up the scattered cards, urging players to stay at the table, and advocating for lasting protection of Kodiak and Afognak's wild lands. Intimately acquainted with the wonders of the archipelago, every contributor has hiked its backcountry, fished its bountiful rivers, marveled at the presence of its giant bears, and worried about what the future may bring.

By joining together in this book, they hope to share their sense of wonder, and to inspire others to join in maintaining and expanding upon the conservation agreements described in *Kodiak Bears & the Exxon Valdez*.

"By week two of the spill it was obvious that Kodiak waters had no protection. Our response options were almost zero. The wildlife was on its own. All we could do was prepare to collect and stack carcasses, and maintain the chain of custody for the criminal prosecution sure to come against Exxon."

—JAY BELLINGER

Jay Bellinger's career in the U.S. Fish and Wildlife Service spanned twenty-two years before he became steward of the legendary brown bears of Kodiak, Alaska in 1984. Prior to becoming Kodiak National Wildlife Refuge manager, Jay served at six federal wildlife refuges from the Shiawassee NWR in Michigan to the Agassiz NWR in northwest Minnesota, Upper Mississippi River NWR in Illinois, Wichita Mountains NWR in Oklahoma, Medicine Lake NWR in eastern Montana, and the Yukon Delta NWR in western Alaska.

Among the wildlife species he managed during his career were timber wolves, bison, wood ducks, whooping cranes, moose, and mule deer in habitats ranging from marshes to bottomland hardwoods, native grassland prairies, subarctic valleys, and windswept mountains.

Despite this diverse resume, nothing had quite prepared Jay for the water-borne threat to the Kodiak Archipelago when the Exxon Valdez ran hard aground on Bligh Reef in Prince William Sound on March 24, 1989.

In 1998, Jay won the prestigious Paul Kroegel Award given annually by the National Wildlife Refuge Association and the National Audubon Society in recognition of both his career achievements and his leadership in facilitating the largest land acquisition by purchase in the history of the National Wildlife Refuge System.

*View toward Prince William Sound from the Barren Islands,
the northernmost part of the Kodiak Archipelago (USFWS).*

CHAPTER I

KODIAK'S OIL SPILL SUMMER

JAY BELLINGER

When the Kodiak Brown Bear Trust asked me to contribute a chapter to *Kodiak Bears & the Exxon Valdez,* I gladly accepted. The book would document how and why the EVOS Trustee Council allocated $250 million from the $1 billion *Exxon Valdez* settlement to protect habitat on 376,000 acres of private land in the Kodiak Archipelago. Helping brown bears wasn't an objective of oil spill restoration because there was no evidence that bears were harmed by the oil. Kodiak's bears ate many oiled carcasses on the beaches in 1989, but no bear mortality was ever attributed to oil ingestion. The only known bear fatality of the oil spill was a brown bear shot by a nervous clean-up crew on the Katmai coast.

Yet despite the bears' lack of oil spill injury, the coastal and riverine areas on Kodiak and Afognak protected by EVOS restoration were world class brown bear habitat. These privately owned lands were subject to development and therefore targeted for EVOS restoration because they were and are important habitat for other fish and wildlife species that were injured by the oil spill—species such as pink and sockeye salmon, bald eagles, marbled murrelet, harbor seals, and river otters. In short, Kodiak's bears got a habitat protection windfall from the EVOS restoration plan's objective of aiding the recovery of oil spill injured fish and wildlife through the permanent protection of their breeding, nesting, and feeding habitat.

While I was pleased to have had a role in bringing about these habitat protection successes, my enthusiasm for the Trust's book waned when I was assigned the lead chapter of *Kodiak Bears & the Exxon Valdez,* the chapter describing the spill itself. In reflecting on my emotional unease

I discovered just how hard I had slammed the door on the memories of the *Exxon Valdez,* and how successful I've been in repressing the shock and disgust I felt from being up close and personal with the nation's worst environmental accident.

The nightmarish images of mass wildlife death and acute social disruption that visited our bustling fishing town had gradually diminished. The frustration of being overrun by outsiders—Exxon personnel, politicians, clean-up contractors, disaster hustlers, and journalists—was not something I wanted to relive. While there were many fine people from all the above groups—Exxon employees included—it is not an experience that people who choose to live in Kodiak enjoy. As a community we suffer our legendary rain, wind, and fog, but people who make Kodiak home can stand bad weather. We value the isolation and the protection of our resources that is a byproduct of being in a place that has been accurately called "cold, wet, and remote." We put up with the weather knowing that a week's worth of good weather on Kodiak is worth a month almost anywhere else.

But the Trust persisted in their request. "How better could such tragedy be understood and avoided in the future than by hearing the story from those who lived it and were most impacted?" And so the following account is a sketch from an admittedly patchy memory, offered with equal doses of reluctance and hope.

THERE'S AN OIL TANKER ON THE ROCKS IN PRINCE WILLIAM SOUND!

The *Exxon Valdez* ran hard aground on Bligh Reef at high tide in the early hours of Friday, March 24, 1989. As the tide fell and the water receded from the cracks in the supertanker's hull, an estimated eleven million gallons of North Slope crude oil gushed into Prince William Sound.

I'm sure I heard about it that Friday, but in the beginning my reaction was probably no different than that of anyone else living on Kodiak Island, or even in the Lower 48 states. The wreck of the *Exxon Valdez* was a needless human mistake that might or might not become a tragedy for wildlife. But either way, it was a tragedy somewhere else—in this case 240 miles away.

Over the weekend my knowledge of the spill was limited to nightly news reports. Going into work on Monday, I was focused as usual on the business of managing the refuge. The spill was the hot topic among refuge staff over morning coffee, though our apprehension about it remained low. By then the oil had been in the water a little more than 72 hours. None of us knew how much oil was spilled, nor did we know that attempts by the U.S. Coast Guard and Exxon to contain it were failing.

Though the weather in Prince William Sound was calm over the weekend, the oil slick had spread twenty miles in three days. Exxon and the Coast Guard proclaimed it "manageable." The scenario changed dramatically on Monday, when 70-mile-per-hour northeast winds developed, and then continued for another day. The slick was on the move, pushed rapidly south by southwest away from the crippled supertanker.

Between Monday, March 27, and Wednesday, the 29th, the eleven million-gallon slick traveled twenty miles each day. All efforts to stop it were failing. Oil engulfed the islands and shores of southwestern Prince William Sound, then entered Montague Strait, where the Sound empties into the Gulf of Alaska (see map page 23).

A call came in from someone at the National Marine Fisheries Service's Kodiak office. "From watching this thing, I wonder if we shouldn't get together and talk about a plan for what we might do down here to protect the resources." I agreed. It was time.

On March 30, a Kodiak group including representatives from the Alaska Department of Fish and Game, Alaska State Parks, Alaska Department of Environmental Conservation, National Oceanic and Atmospheric Administration, National Marine Fisheries Service Law Enforcement, and the Alaska State Troopers Fish and Wildlife protection staff met for the first time.

Somebody furnished a sea current chart for the region. From this we learned the dominant Gulf of Alaska currents traveled from east to west past Prince William Sound, and then south by southwest along the Kenai Peninsula. Here the currents divide, some moving north into Cook Inlet, to be influenced by enormous tidal action, while the largest and strongest currents continue southwest, past the Barren Islands and down the west side of Kodiak in the Shelikof Strait where it eddies out below Kodiak Island south of the Trinity Islands.

This counter-clockwise flow of water in the Gulf of Alaska is known as the Alaskan Gyre. After reviewing the current chart, everyone in the room was thinking the same thing: if conditions are normal, there is no way this oil is going to miss us. We could see we were likely going to get smeared if it couldn't be stopped. And we all knew that nobody was stopping it despite the assurances from Exxon executive Frank Iarossi that Kodiak had nothing to worry about. There were no orders as of yet from the upper reaches of our respective chains of command, but we all agreed it would be wise to at least take a look at where seabirds and marine mammals were concentrated, just in case.

The next morning we had planes in the air, mapping the whereabouts of sea otters, seabirds, and other wildlife in the waters surrounding the northern half of the Kodiak Archipelago. The fly-overs confirmed our expectations: spring migration of seabirds was in full swing and they were mingling with resident birds and wildlife and they were spread far and wide.

In going down the list of possible responses, we first considered trying to scare wildlife away from the oil. We decided the unpredictable path of the oil, along with the greatly dispersed wildlife, would make that all but impossible. We considered "booming off " bays and inlets with floating barriers of absorbent materials to soak up the oil. This would create a series of safe havens which wildlife might discover. The problem with this plan was the lack of available resources. In hard-hit Prince William Sound, clean-up crews were just getting deployed and already lacked sufficient boom material. We understood, too, that the rougher water around Kodiak and the Alaska Peninsula would make booms less effective than in the calmer bays, coves, and inlets of Prince William Sound.

When it came to equipment, we had no skimmer vessels to vacuum and separate oil from water—all available skimmers were either at work in Prince William Sound or en route from all over the world.

A NEW CHAIN OF COMMAND

Within the first week of the spill, the Bush administration decided against federalizing the oil spill response, opting instead for a pledge by Exxon to take charge and pay all costs.

The Exxon public relations machine went into high gear. Exxon president Lawrence Rawl delivered a promise: the giant corporation, he said, would meet every obligation associated with the spill, and in the process "make everyone whole." These words, for better or worse, would become a benchmark; they would resonate with each family, each life thrown into turmoil. Most of the people who later found fault with Exxon's handling of the crisis were also critical of the Bush administration's decision to keep it in corporate hands.

The administration's decision had immediate consequences for my authority and ability to enforce policy. The established federal chain of command I operated within under normal conditions—from Kodiak, to the USFWS' Region 7 office in Anchorage—was short-circuited. The day after our first aerial surveys, I received a call from the USFWS regional office that would change my life for the next six months. I was instructed to hand over management duties of Kodiak NWR to the assistant manager; from that day on, I would serve as on-site USFWS representative for this section of the spill.

My responsibility was to cover USFWS trust responsibilities for the southern half of the oil spill region. My sphere of influence stretched from the Barren Islands at the northern boundary of the Kodiak Island Borough, south to the Trinity Islands below Kodiak, and west over to the Alaska Peninsula on the western shore of Shelikof Strait.

This sizeable area was at the moment still free of oil. It spanned more than 1,000 miles of coastline. It included some of the world's most productive marine and coastal ecosystems. Much of this land was in public hands—the entire Kodiak NWR, the eastern coasts of Katmai National Park and Preserve; Becharof NWR, Alaska Peninsula NWR, Aniakchak National Monument and Preserve on the Alaska Peninsula, several units of the Alaska State Park System, and dozens of islands in the Alaska Maritime NWR.

Saddled with a new and confusing chain of command, the Kodiak response team I served on with representatives from state and federal wildlife agencies consulted with Kodiak City Mayor Bob Brodie and Kodiak Island Borough Mayor Jerome Selby. They requested that Exxon authorize use of Kodiak Island's commercial fishing fleet to sweep up oil, using nets and buckets if no booms were available, as was being done in Prince William Sound. Exxon said no. It was a decision that infuriated most commercial fishermen, but it demonstrated who was in charge, and how little power the Kodiak response team and the mayors really had.

Most of the fishing boats remained in port. Through much of the 1980s, the Kodiak Island fleet was Alaska's and one of the nation's top commercial ports. Preparations were under way for the opening of herring season in mid-April. The hearts and minds of fishermen were also focused on what they hoped would be a strong salmon season, perhaps one to rival 1988, the best in the history of Alaska's commercial salmon fishery. It is difficult to overstate how promising the 1989 salmon season looked to both veterans and newcomers alike. While nets were made ready and crews hired on, expectations along the docks were soaring.

DISASTER IN THE BARREN ISLANDS

By week two of the spill, it was obvious that Kodiak waters had no protection. Our response options were almost zero. The wildlife was on its own. All we could do was prepare to collect and stack carcasses, and maintain the chain of custody for the criminal prosecution sure to come later against Exxon.

Petroleum scientists and engineers from around the world converged on Exxon's response headquarters in the town of Valdez. Dozens of theories were offered about how the oil would behave and how long its killing power would last. Previous spills, such as the *Amoco Cadiz* on France's Normandy coast, or spills from offshore well blow-outs near Texas and California, had devastated wildlife. In every case it was the same: big spills equaled big die-offs for every living thing, whether in the water or on the beaches. And here we had a lot more wildlife.

On the eve of the oil spill's entry into Gulf of Alaska waters from Prince William Sound, we pinned our hopes to chances that the oil would miss us, or possibly evaporate and dissolve, as some were predicting. We knew the Gulf of Alaska's coastal current would direct most of the slick down the Shelikof Strait, and we knew that wind direction would be a critical factor in determining the route and speed of the slick. Following endless weather updates became a major pastime. The *Anchorage Daily News* ran daily maps showing the progress of the oil. Reporters and camera crews from every network had arrived to document the devastation in Prince William Sound.

With no real authority there was virtually nothing to do but wait and we began devising best- and worst-case scenarios.

In a best-case scenario for Kodiak, we hoped for a strong easterly wind to move the oil across lower Cook Inlet into Kamishak Bay, along the coast of the Alaska Peninsula north of Katmai National Park. As horrendous as that would be for that area, wildlife populations were not as abundant there as in coastal Gulf of Alaska. There were also far fewer people, with a much smaller commercial fishery than in Kodiak. Wildlife, human, and economic impacts would be far less dramatic and costly.

In a second best-case scenario, gale-force northeast winds would quickly push the slick down the Shelikof Strait—possibly right past the Kodiak Archipelago and the Alaska Peninsula—without widening it too much. From there, the oil would disperse into the Gulf of Alaska. It was unlikely the oil would miss either, let alone both shores of the Strait, but it seemed at least possible. The shape of the slick, along with wind speed and direction, would be the crucial variables.

A third, unlikely positive scenario involved a strong, sustained west wind, powerful enough to overcome the Gulf's coastal current. An event such as this could move the oil east of the Kodiak Archipelago into the central Gulf.

In one worst-case scenario, the slick would disperse over a wide area, and light winds would allow the current to move it slowly south and west, lingering in our waters for a long time. Once here, it would slop back and forth through Shuyak, Raspberry, and Kupreanof Straits, driven by tidal action, fouling both sides of the Archipelago.

Another important question involved oil toxicity, and how it might change. Nearly all of the scientists agreed that as the oil remained in water, it continued to lose its killing power. "Weathering" allowed the deadlier components—benzene, ethylbenzene, toulene and xylene—to either evaporate or disperse into less deadly concentrations. [1]

For people all over the world, the lasting images of the *Exxon Valdez* spill formed over the first week following the wreck. The slick was at its thickest and had completely inundated the picturesque islands, bays, coves, and inlets of Prince William Sound. Televised images of this natural splendor smeared by America's worst environmental disaster drove the public's sense of outrage to fever pitch.

What is virtually unknown by the general public, or even most Alaskans, is that the balance of the oil spill that escaped Prince William Sound would prove more deadly to wildlife from a body count perspective. In addition to the great quantities of oil that smothered southwestern Prince William Sound, approximately two million gallons flowed through Montague Strait into the northern Gulf of Alaska. Fish and wildlife populations are notably higher in this region, especially seabird populations—and in particular, the common murre.

By the time the oil arrived, these hardy colonial nesting birds were completing their spring migration back to Alaska. Thousands of murres drifted in flocks on the water, feeding in lower Cook Inlet and around the Barren Islands prior to inhabiting nest sites on nearby cliffs.

By March 30th, oil had arrived in the Gulf of Alaska. For the next week, north and northeast winds spread the slick; it inched slowly toward the west, but remained out in the coastal currents, lingering twelve to twenty miles off the south coast of the Kenai Peninsula. Then from April 7 through 9, a shift brought south-southwest winds, and disaster struck again: oil inundated the offshore islands, capes, and headlands along the full length of Kenai Fiords National Park. But luckily the winds were not strong enough to push large amounts of oil deep inside Kenai's spectacular fiords.

The coastal current took over again, carrying the slick south by southwest, until on April 10, a Gulf of Alaska storm raised powerful northeast winds that dispersed the oil, breaking it into large patches. On April 11 oil spread to the southern tip of the Kenai Peninsula, the Chugach

*Common murre colonies on the Barren Islands bore the highest
lethal impact of the oil spill (EVOS Trustee Council).*

Islands, and the Kennedy Entrance to Lower Cook Inlet. The powerful tides and currents of the Inlet churned the blackish mass and spread it further. Most of the oil then moved southwest, continuing toward the Barren Islands. The worst-case scenario for Kodiak and the Alaska Peninsula looked more and more likely.

On April 13, a small 20-by-20-foot slick caught the eye of an aerial surveyor near Shuyak Island. On April 14th the *Kodiak Daily Mirror* featured a banner headline: **OIL SOUTH OF KHUYAK, FLIGHT CONFIRMS, IT'S THICK, IT'S GOOEY, IT'S DEFINITELY HERE.**

The rest of the slick remained off the southern tip of the Kenai Peninsula. Between April 17 and 21 the southern Kenai coast received a heavy hit. Some oil moved north into Cook Inlet.

As predicted by experts, the oil was "weathering " now, changing its composition. The action of waves forced air bubbles into the patches and globs, causing them to emulsify; once-liquid crude oil was transformed into a brown goo that became known as "mousse," as it bore a strong resemblance to the color and consistency of that chocolate dessert.

Although I didn't know it at the time, a field survey of the oil spill's impact on marine birds by FWS biologists John F. Piatt et. al. would find convincing evidence that mid-April was the spill's most lethal period for wildlife. Common murre colonies on southern Kenai Peninsula, the Chugach Islands, and especially the Barren Islands experienced the highest mortalities of any species of wildlife in the spill region.

The figures are staggering. Piatt and his associates projected 100,000 to 300,000 seabirds were killed during mid-April, the vast majority of which were common murres. These mortalities occurred outside of Prince William Sound, and comprised 88 percent of the spill 's entire toll on seabirds from March 24 through August 1. The large variable of 200,000 was due to uncertainties in extrapolating the total number from the nearly 20,000 bird carcasses found on the beaches of the Barren Islands (2,163), the Alaska Peninsula (8,881), and the Kodiak Archipelago (8,548). Researchers assumed, for example, that most bird carcasses either sank or were eaten by predators.

While it seems counter-intuitive, just 20 percent of the oil spilled was responsible for 80 percent of all wildlife killed. The death toll

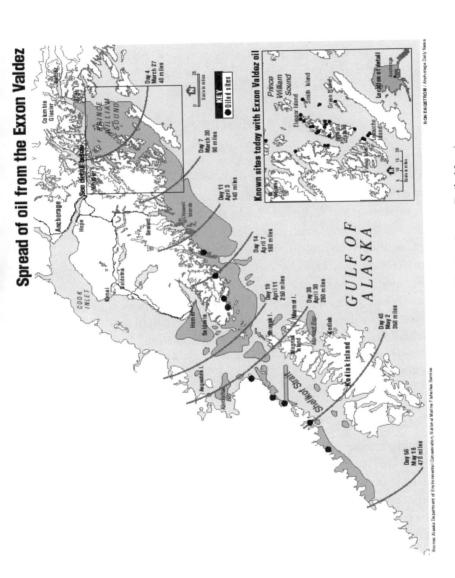

The spread of oil from the Exxon Valdez *(Anchorage Daily News)*

apparently lessened dramatically once the slick passed the Barren Islands. But the evidence is clear that 75 percent of all fish and wildlife mortality in the Kodiak region actually occurred before most of the oil reached the shores of the Kodiak Island. Beach crews in Kodiak collected thousands of bird carcasses over the summer, but the majority of these were casualties from the mid-April kill in the Barren Islands.

KODIAK'S OIL SPILL SUMMER

Over the last two weeks of April, any remaining oil that didn't drift into Cook Inlet made its way to the waters off Kodiak and the Alaska Peninsula. The flow pattern followed the dominant currents, moving south by southwest. Wind and tides broke the slick into hundreds of patches of varying size and composition, with thousands of "mousse clusters " and countless "tar balls. " Oil sheen, a thin, multi-colored film on the water's surface, was another common sight around Kodiak throughout the summer.

The irregular coastlines of Kodiak and the Alaska Peninsula were ideal traps for passing oil. Capes and headlands collected hunks the size of football fields, along with thousands of smaller formations. Beaches on both sides of the Shelikof Strait were smeared, with the Alaska Peninsula getting the worst of it— a number of areas there featured thick weathered crude oil and looked as bad as the worst-hit areas of Prince William Sound.

Some oil split away from the main slick when it was still north of Kodiak, and traveled down the east side of the archipelago. Oil that passed below Kodiak from the Shelikof often moved north, collecting on Kodiak's southeastern beaches whenever rising tides and southeasterly winds pushed it ashore. Damage was worst on beaches that naturally collected the most sea-borne debris. For example, a good driftwood beach was always more heavily oiled than other areas.

As representatives from Exxon, the U.S. Coast Guard, and state and federal agencies flooded into Kodiak, the once-sleepy town resembled the staging area for a military invasion. Helicopters and planes droned overhead. Concerned residents packed meeting halls every day. Nearly all statements from authorities, myself included, were heavily bracketed with variables and contingencies. The signature phrase of that summer was *"I don't know, I'll get back to you."*

I began a sixteen-hour-a-day, seven-day-a-week work routine. It wouldn't end until September, a personal record I hope I'll never break. My title of On-site Representative In Charge of Clean-up for the U.S. Fish and Wildlife Service had a powerful sound, but not much more. Exxon and its subcontractor, Veco International, made all key decisions. The most critical issues involved spending money. Falling into this category were matters such as the size, number, and deployment of beach crews, as well as the number and composition of boats chartered for clean-up duties.

The mayor of Kodiak City, Bob Brodie, was named head of the "Oiled Mayors" group, which represented the twenty two cities and villages in the spill region. Brodie, along with Kodiak Island Borough Mayor Jerome Selby, were extremely capable and persistent advocates for Kodiak's human and economic needs. They skillfully applied varying levels of pressure and cooperation toward Exxon and occasionally pried some dollars loose for the community.

Kodiak's population must have jumped from 12,000 to perhaps 15,000 or more. Clean-up efforts peaked in June and didn't wind down until Labor Day. Merchants did a booming business. Grocery stores and marine supply companies scrambled to fill orders, and hotels and B&Bs had probably their best year ever. Most of the commercial fishing fleet, however, sat idle. First the herring season was cancelled in Kodiak waters out of fear the catch would be contaminated. Week after week went by, and salmon season remained closed as well.

Though Exxon was in charge of the clean-up, there remained the possibility of a federal take-over, or a joint state-federal effort, if things got too snarled up. Of course that plan also had its critics too. A few individuals thrived in the black-market atmosphere; others withdrew to varying degrees. Fishermen and their families were under extreme financial stress. Suicides were in the news. Throughout the community, alcohol abuse, crimes of anger, and mental health problems exploded.

A study commissioned by the "Oiled Mayors" analyzed economic, social, and psychological effects on residents in the spill region, and found three general, adverse experiences in these communities:

- A fundamental disruption of usual ways of living, including one's sense of personal health and well-being.
- Loss of personal and community control over the daily events of living and doing business.
- Displacement of usual and expected actions, plans, and resources required as a response to the demands of the oil spill and clean-up.

Psychological effects associated with exposure to the oil spill and its aftermath included increased occurrence of depression, general anxiety disorder (GAD), and Post-Traumatic Stress Disorder (PTSD).

Substance abuse and domestic violence increased significantly. For example, in comparison to non-affected communities in Alaska, spill-affected communities experienced:

- 11.4 times more drinking.
- 7.4 times more drug use.
- 11.6 times more domestic violence.

The spill took its toll, both on those involved in clean-up efforts and citizens who attended the endless public meetings. Suspicion and mistrust of Exxon and the government were rampant. Wild theories circulated about the whole spill being premeditated to test population control. There was widespread fear regarding the long-term toxicity of the oil. The people of Kodiak had survived more than their share of natural disasters—earthquakes, tidal waves, and five feet of volcanic ash following the 1912 Katmai eruption—but this crisis felt different. It was an unnatural disaster.

Work was at least one form of release, and many people in Kodiak rallied together. Beach clean-up was under way before Exxon authorized crews and began hiring people. Out on the water, mousse and tarballs were far easier for birds and mammals to see and avoid than the oil slick. Even so, the wildlife body count rose steadily, the totals tracked and printed by the *Kodiak Daily Mirror* and announced on radio news updates.

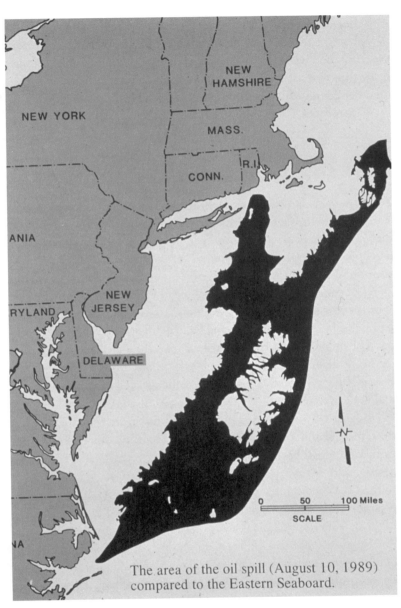

The area of the oil spill (August 10, 1989) compared to the Eastern Seaboard.

The oil spill region superimposed off the eastern shore of the U.S. (EVOS Trustee Council).

The behavior of the oil was by turns predictable and mysterious. Slicks moved from beach to beach by tides, wind, rain storms, and wave action; they came and went, depositing a film that was often invisible. Families made trips to what looked like an unoiled beach for a picnic. The children started out with clean clothes, but invariably returned with oil covering their shoes, pants, and shirts.

KILLING THE WATER

Perhaps the best method of conveying the issues confronting the people of Kodiak during the summer of the spill is to review transcripts of meetings where field reports from state and federal agencies provided updates on clean-up results and a public forum where citizens could speak their mind to a panel.

The panel met weekly and consisted of Exxon Community Liaison John Peavy; Kodiak City Mayor Bob Brodie; and Borough Mayor Jerome Selby, along with state and federal officials and sometimes others. The following excerpts of testimony are from an August 8 meeting of the Kodiak clean-up task force, and an afternoon meeting of the Exxon Valdez Oil Spill Commission, which visited each impacted city and took testimony.

August is a good point at which to capture people's feelings in Kodiak, more than four months after the accident. By this time the commercial salmon fishery was in shambles, having been closed around most of the island. Many commercial fishermen and their families were down to their last financial reserves or already broke. Anxiety and frustration regarding their economic future, along with anger over Exxon's handling of the operation, was at its peak.

Salmon fishermen and the region's Native population are two groups of people with an uncommon connection to, and economic dependency upon, healthy fish and wildlife. By all accounts, these were the people who suffered most. Their livelihoods and lifestyles were turned upside down.

The first excerpts below are representative of daily government updates on the status of clean-up efforts, and reports of where oil was located around Kodiak and the Alaska Peninsula.

"*DEC has been quite busy as usual. We've been out mousse-spotting and have found that there is quite a bit of it moving in on the west side of the island again, around Karluk and on up into Uyak Bay, Hook Point, and that area. We have found some fairly large masses on the beach and we are still out chasing mousse around. And so this seems to be an ongoing event and apparently will be for quite some time yet.*

"*We are also still working the mainland out on the Alaska Peninsula, where we have a helicopter on a daily basis. We have one down in Chignik, and we are also still working back and forth through Shuyak and Afognak and up and down the island here. We have finished pretty well our second major mapping. We are at the point where we are getting real frustrated with mapping, primarily because of the fact that there is just such a large area and we can't really keep up with it.*"

—JOHN HOPKINS
Alaska Department of
Environmental Conservation

"*We have two catcher vessels, the* Columbia, *which is down on Aniakchak now, and the* Winona J. *near Shakun and Kiupalik Islands. In the last three days since we talked here they've picked up twenty-four dead birds and two dead otters. The National Park Service vessel the* Staccato *is enroute to the peninsula. They have four biotechs aboard and they are going to be working the Katmai Bay area for awhile . . . . Up to this date we've had over 400 federal and state employees rotating through our operation. Most of the people are from the Lower 48 and had a strong interest in this operation; we have many, many volunteers trying to get up to work here.*

"*Of the three Exxon vessel groups, the* Arctic Sounder *fleet has a crew of somewhere between 59 and 67. They picked up about 1,600 bags in the last two or three days. The Snowpack fleet is working the Kuliak Bay area and they have about 50 people—they picked up about 150 bags of spoil there and also picked up about nine dead* birds. The Aleutian *fleet is working in the Kashvik area and they have picked up about 783 bags with 53 workers.*

"To date the crews have picked up about 60,000 bags, they've covered about 44 miles of the Katmai Peninsula within the Katmai National Park. To date we've had 7,737 dead birds collected, 32 otters, and about 60,000 bags of spoil.

—ANONYMOUS NATIONAL PARKS SPOKESMAN

"In the past week our dead bird total is up to 17,593 processed through the Kodiak Center. We've processed 143 dead sea otters and 54 dead bald eagles. That number went up by one each in the past week. And we had an eagle brought in from Uganik that was diseased and died here at the treatment facility within hours of arrival. We've had three fresh dead otters that are in for necropsy, and we expect those results within 24 hours. We are today sending up 24 fresh dead seabirds taken out of the tide rips to our morgue facilities. As far as seabirds, we are seeing a shift away from murres and toward fork-tailed storm petrels and shearwaters. We'll be reporting to you later on what we think these changes mean and why we are getting so many fresh dead lately."

—PAUL BURKE
U.S. Fish and Wildlife Service

"We currently have 10 test fishing vessels active. Just to mention a few of the high points here, the Ugak Bay area reported light impact, light sheen with occasional fresh mousse two to four inches in diameter yesterday. And then the Gold Nugget reported very light bands of sheen with mousse one to five inches in diameter; this extended from Gull Cape Lagoon to Dangerous Cape.

"In Kiliuda Bay, a half-mile south of Dangerous Cape, mousse was found in the tide streaks, also dead birds, vegetation, et cetera, and they did find mousse in that area one to eight inches in diameter, in streaks extending as long as a mile. Uganik Bay and the outer capes

between Miners Point and Cape Kuiliuk showed light to moderate impact to very light, silver sheens with two- to four-inch-diameter mousse. The Rocky Point to Cape Karluk area has light impact, silver sheen with frequent mousse balls up to two inches in diameter off of Rocky Point.

"Cape Karluk to Cape Ikolik had light impacts of sheen with some mousse found at Ikolik and Bear Rocks. One area we thought was starting to show some real positive signs and had for awhile was the Red River area south to Cape Alitak. We did get hit with impacts of mousse yesterday in that area as well. And again these were found not only on the beach but in the tide streaks.

"Cape Alitak to Cape Trinity including inner Alitak Bay, had light impacts of sheen reported at Cape Alitak, Tanner Head and Moser Bay, Fox Island, Cape Hepburn and Portage. Again, new mousse, some of which was as large as ten inches in diameter. The last area that received new hits was over on the mainland, the north mainland district, light to moderate sheen reported from Swikshak to Kaflia Bay with mousse reported at Hallo Bay and Cape Nukshak.

"Another item—we decided that most of the booms around the island with a few exceptions should probably be out of the water on or about the 15th of August. The rationale is trying to prevent siltation, where booms silt in to the point where fish cannot pass. We've recommended that booms on the road systems be maintained until the sport season is over. There are appreciable amounts of mousse materials still hitting those systems on the road, and we think it is best to try to reduce man's interaction with that to the degree we can.

"Kitoi Bay fishery, the catch of pink salmon there now has exceeded 4 million, it is still coming along pretty well and may end up somewhere between 5 and 6 million total harvest. Again there is oil material still moving in that area. We are finding it on the outside boom in Kitoi Bay. I mentioned to Exxon this morning the need to move some of those crews back in to keep that stuff cleared off the boom."

—LARRY NICHOLSON
Alaska Department of Fish and Game

*"As for the village clean-up crews, yesterday Ouzinkie gathered 13
bags of oiled material, their day was cut short because of a village
meeting. In Port Lions there were 154 bags of material collected. Old
Harbor 42 bags of material and we were also there for a meeting, so
the day was cut a bit short. Karluk had 200 bags of material were
collected. Larsen Bay had 200 bags of material and Akhiok 45 bags.
On the road system, crews at Pillar Creek that had worked
Monashka Bay, Abercrombie Lake. . .there were 26 people involved
in the clean-up and they gathered 226 bags of material."*

—JOHN PEAVY
Exxon Community Liaison

After these morning government reports, citizens typically would
have the opportunity to speak and address questions to the Exxon representative, as well as other panel members. Here, an anonymous ques-
tioner addresses Exxon liaison John Peavy.

ANONYMOUS: "Are you planning to send any clean-up crews or
clean-up materials to Tugidak Island? Folks there have been pretty heavily impacted."

PEAVY: "I talked to NOAA this morning about that. We have no plans
at this time to take anyone to Tugidak. We have had survey teams down
there to evaluate the island but at this time there are no plans to send a
team to that location."

ANONYMOUS: "Can I ask why?"

PEAVY: "For a couple of reasons. One, access was originally a problem.
The second is that the scat team's assessment of that area is that it was
very lightly hit."

ANONYMOUS: "We've had a lot of dead birds wash up there. I was there
yesterday and talked to a lady."

PEAVY: "We have operations under way to make sure those birds are re-covered, so that part I know is going to occur, but as far as beach clean-up operations, there is no plan at this time."

The next exchange is between Kodiak resident Kristin Stahl Johnson, an environmental leader and wife of a commercial fisherman, Exxon's John Peavy, borough mayor Jerome Selby, and Kodiak fishing crew mem-ber Mike Milligan. The issue raised by Johnson questions why Exxon re-mained opposed to using the Kodiak seine fleet to clean beaches at re-mote points around Kodiak Island.

Local residents believed the salmon seiners could be effective in clean-ing the hundreds of hard-to-reach, remote beach areas along the archi-pelago and on the Alaska Peninsula. These areas were often inaccessible to anything but small boats and rubber rafts and the amount of oil on these areas didn't justify a large crew.

Advocates for hiring the seine fleet also argued that the more that were hired the better off this hard-hit economic sector would be, given the closure of most of Kodiak's salmon fishery. To many people, this re-sponse would be part of fulfilling Exxon's often-used pledge to "make people whole." Exxon hired up to twenty seiners at a time (out of a fleet of 400) to cruise local waters searching for mousse and tarballs in the tide rips or anywhere they could find them and collecting them from the water with buckets and dip nets.

JOHNSON: "What is the status of the negotiations on getting the sein-ers and dual purpose [fishing boats] on the beach and in the water? Talk to just about any one of the guys on the big boats that have been out all sum-mer and they say 'why don't we have more seiners out here, you guys could do a much more effective job getting it [oil] on the beach than we can?'"

PEAVY: "As to the dual purpose of the seine fleet, we have been provided a proposal. We still believe that the most effective way to use the seiners is in the original concept which was to have them do free-floating oil. We are trying to work with them to get them into smaller groups—trying to get them into areas where they might be able to work in the rough water during calm times, and possibly into the bays during rough weather. That won't always occur but we still believe the most effective way to utilize that crew is to work free-floating oil.

JOHNSON: "I'd like to contest, disagree, whatever, on what the best use of the seine fleet is. If you are not going to let these guys work the beaches, guys who always work on the beaches all year long, know how to work the beaches, know how to get in and off them safer than almost anybody else does. . . ."

PEAVY: "We have decided to utilize their vessels. We are paying vessel charters for those seiners. . . ."

JOHNSON: "But you are not utilizing your resource, you are not utilizing the seine fleet which are the most effective. . . ."

PEAVY: "Let me finish what I was trying to say to you. Okay? Basically what has happened is we have looked at that process. We've determined that as long as we are willing to pay for the vessel and the crew, we would like them to be involved in clean-up of free-floating materials. If they find themselves having to be on the beach all the time because of weather, then what we are doing is basically paying for a very small number of people to be transported by boat to a beach, and we would rather have our beach crews get involved in that process.

JOHNSON: "You aren't hearing me. It is very clear that you don't understand the nature of this fleet or the people that are in it, and you are not allowing for the beaches to get cleaned up. You are not doing what the community wants done. You are doing what Exxon wants done and you are not listening to us, and it is real clear."

MAYOR SELBY: "I think one of the things that you folks (Exxon) may have missed on that, and that is why we keep asking you to take a look at it, is the fact that there are a number of small lagoons and coves and areas that have oil on them, and it's just not cost-effective, it doesn't make sense to take a twenty-person crew in there. You will spend more time moving them on and off the beach than they spend cleaning it. But these guys [the seine fleet] can zip in there and get closer because they are smaller vessels, they can go in with their four or five folks and clean up and be out of there in a day."

PEAVY: "You have asked that and that argument has been addressed. I talked to (Exxon) operations this morning. The answer is no, not at this time. But that doesn't mean that we won't once we feel that storms are starting to come up in such a manner that we're having a lot of lost time. But right now they are sticking with what they believe is the correct way to utilize that crew."

MILLIGAN: "I disagree with what the seine group is being used for. I feel that Exxon is using the seine group to document that there is not that much oil in the water. Since nobody is allowed on the beaches they are not going to see what's there. The oil is incredibly dispersed. I think everybody realizes that. We are not going to find thirty-yard mats of mousse anywhere. The oil is now dispersed. It collects on the beaches. There are a lot of beaches that have not been visited. There are a lot of beaches that can't be surveyed because you can't land a helicopter on them. Exxon is not paying to do many surveys by boat. The best way to survey those beaches would be by the seine fleet. I could take you right now to beaches that you could spend all summer cleaning up and you wouldn't be able to clean them, because the same weather that brings the mousse in also buries it under the gravel.

"And what I see Exxon doing here is using the seine fleet to document that there is not that much oil out in the water, and because nobody wants to blow their charter with Exxon, nobody is going to admit to going to the beaches.

"The beaches are where the oil is. The oil is in the popweed. You can look at a beach from a quarter-mile away and know where you are going to fill a bucket—you're going to fill a bucket in that thirty-yard section of popweed. You're going to get the fresh mousse balls coming in. You could take a boat and spend fifty gallons of fuel (in open water) to get a coffee can full of tarballs. But if you go to the beach, you can shut the boat off and go to the beach in the skiff. And you can fill a couple of buckets. But Exxon doesn't want people to know what's on the beaches, and there is oil buried in the beaches and it is recoverable oil.

"No, I don't think things are going to return to a pristine quality. We've been oiled. Nature is going to have to do a lot of the work. I can see that, but there is recoverable mousse on the beaches right now."

This exchange is valuable because it reveals two things: the kind of dialogue that went on all summer, and the power Exxon held when it came to resolving clean-up issues. The seine fleet never was used in the manner requested by Johnson, Selby, and Milligan, and there was no recourse for the public to resolve such disputes. The power of public institutions was basically non-existent.

The above dialogue also reveals the standard operating procedure of Exxon. If they felt cornered in a debate, their spokesperson would promise to have the issue reviewed by higher authorities elsewhere in the Exxon bureaucracy. It was rare for these anonymous higher authorities to override a decision by the field representatives. The following personal testimony provides another snap-shot look at how individuals felt when confronting Exxon's authority.

PAT MCLAIN: "I'm a Kodiak resident for approximately 15 years. For the last three or four months I've been doing work on Tugidak Island, which Exxon does not want to clean up. I've been through many, many meetings and there have been a lot of promises made but they've never, ever done anything on it. And it's getting very serious down there. I talked to some of my people this morning and in the last two days they (six people) have picked up between 3,000 and 4,000 pounds of mousse and dead birds, sea otters, and its a real serious problem down there. Exxon has agreed to pick it up and a Fish and Game boat has been picking things up, but there is only one point on the island they can do it and that's in the lagoon, it's called pick-up point, and it's the only place you can land a boat safely. Getting around that island and working is just about impossible doing it from a boat. You have to do it from a land-based operation. But it has killed everything down there, a lot of birds. They are saying a couple thousand birds, I would say probably 15,000 birds have died down there which equals as much as they say the whole impact is. I've got pictures of piles of birds. Nine dead whales, you can't talk about. It's kind of serious. I have a copy of Don Garber's log here when the oil first hit—when he was crying for help and not getting anything but promises, 'Yeah we'll be out to see you.' And it never happened. I heard the reason was a federal gag order from the U.S. Attorney General's office because of the dead whales and there was a lawsuit over them. So they could not talk about the whales, but there are seals molting down there that have oil all over them, everything's got oil on it, nothing is clean, and they are going to be leaving here now. I don't understand why they are being allowed to leave. Admiral Yost said that Exxon would do anything that they told them to do. Well, they just said they're leaving on the 15th of September whether or not it is cleaned up. It doesn't make sense.

"Tugidak is a very critical area for fishing. It has a crabber running down there right now, there's a lot of crabbing going on and it is effecting everything. The way that island is situated the water swirls in that area, so you get a lot of death down there. Plus, the crew that is working down there were led to believe by me, through Exxon, that they were going to be paid, but Exxon denies that they ever said a word about it, so they are still working with no thought of getting a paycheck.

"I don't believe anything Exxon says. I think they are a bunch of very dishonest people. And I believe that the federal government should take this over and do it right, clean it up. Because this oil is going to be here a long, long time. The oil from the French *Amoco Cadiz* took five years before it dissipated enough to where any life came back, and this water is a lot different— it is a lot colder. It's going to take much longer in my belief.

"They are cleaning up tarballs with a force of 400, with some people covering 7,000 miles of beaches. That is just unreal. You could work them night and day for ten years and they wouldn't get it all. More people are needed, and it needs to be done right. They need the sweepers to pick them up out here and they haven't used them here to my knowledge and if the Coast Guard lets them get out of here, they'll never be back."

QUESTION FROM THE PANEL: "How come Exxon says your crew shouldn't be paid even though they were picking up oil?"

MCLAIN: "They said that we were never hired, even though they sent me to their claims office and told me how to fill out the claims so we would be reimbursed, and then evidently something went wrong with that. So they just kind of kept telling me, 'Well we've got to clean up the island sooner or later, and you live there, you'll clean it up,' and I was informed that if it was ever cleaned up it would be done by Veco, Veco does all clean-up."

QUESTION FROM THE PANEL: " Would you be willing to say for us what you think you are losing this summer?"

MCLAIN: "I borrowed $56,000 to do this on their promises."

And so it went that oil spill summer.

The frustrations in Kodiak were highest among commercial fishermen, rural villages that rely on subsistence, and fish and wildlife professionals. Of course anyone with a deeply felt attachment to nature suffered the oil spill like a personal insult from the modern world, a world all of us thought we lived far enough away from. We were wrong, and our comforting sense of remoteness and isolation living on Kodiak diminished without our consent. Walter Meganack, a Native leader from Prince William Sound, perhaps captured our sense of bewilderment and foreboding best when he said, "I never thought they could kill the water."

Exxon pulled out their Kodiak operation in September, and I handed off any future involvement with clean-up to members of my staff the next year. Winter storms, pounding surf, and normal weathering have eliminated nearly all visible oil residue on Kodiak, although I'm certain the beaches on Shuyak and Afognak Island and the Katmai Coast have vestiges of the oil spill if you search for it.

The wildlife species that were in trouble before the spill remain in trouble—especially harbor seals, harlequin ducks, and marbled murrelets, and their recovery from the spill remains in doubt.

REFERENCE

[1] *Degrees of Disaster,* by Jeff Wheelwright

OIL SPILL PICTORIAL
Photos Courtesy of the *Kodiak Daily Mirror*

*Vice President Dan Quayle expressed official dismay at an
Anchorage press conference soon after the oil spill.*

*Transportation Secretary Samuel Skinner (right) arrives at
Kodiak in a U.S. Coast Guard C-130.*

Makeshift booms were deployed in hopes of keeping oil out of sensitive bays.

Kodiak Borough mayor Jerome Selby (left) and U.S. Senator Ted Stevens ponder disaster options. Stevens opposed putting Exxon in charge of the clean-up.

Oil comes ashore on Kodiak.

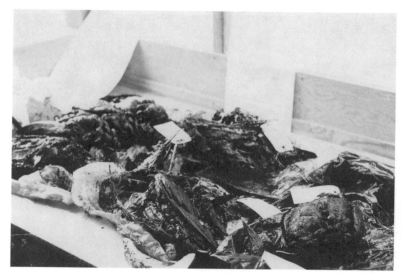

Sea bird carcasses.

Rescue teams saved some wildlife.

The dead bird count in Kodiak was twice as high as Prince William Sound.

Oiled bald eagle in captivity.

Public outrage seethed as Exxon pledged to "make everyone whole."

"From a Native corporation's point of view we faced uncertainty but our attitude began to shift as 1990 began. We'd taken a hard shot economically but we'd found our voice."

—EMIL CHRISTIANSEN

Old Harbor Native Corporation was sixteen years old when the Exxon Valdez *disaster occurred. The wreck plunged a fishing village of 300 into bewilderment and economic free-fall, but the spill's aftermath gave its corporation's shareholders a monumental opportunity to negotiate a wildlife habitat transaction that would honor their Alutiiq forebearers and provide future generations with a stake in the modern economy.*

Like other Alaska Native village corporations, established pursuant to and as envisioned in the Alaska Native Claims Settlement Act, Old Harbor Native Corporation (OHNC) was guided by a blend of cultural, community, and economic considerations; and like many village corporations, it was economically challenged in 1989. Asset management and shareholder benefits are among a Native corporation's purposes, yet its board of directors are guided in decision-making by 7,500 year-old tribal roots in one of the North Pacific's richest maritime areas.

This chapter includes OHNC president Emil Christiansen's story of the Exxon Valdez *disaster and the resulting Kodiak fish and wildlife habitat conservation agreements as conveyed to and recounted by Tim Richardson, executive director of the Kodiak Brown Bear Trust.*

Derelict salmon boat at Old Harbor. Kodiak's small boat fleet was the hardest hit economic sector of the oil spill (Scott Stouder).

CHAPTER 2

AN ALUTIIQ PERSPECTIVE

EMIL CHRISTIANSEN

Memories of the *Exxon Valdez* oil spill come easy—and hard. I first heard of the spill while at the Hoquiam Boat Yard near Aberdeen, Washington waiting to take ownership of my newly built seiner christened the *Carla Rae C.* The boat builder signed over the papers and said, "Good luck. Too bad you won't be fishing this year."

"Yeah, right," I responded, thinking it was a joke. But he was predicting the oil spill in Prince William Sound would close Kodiak's salmon season. As I navigated north through Alaska's Inside Passage and across the northern Gulf of Alaska I couldn't help thinking of the boat builder's words—so I was worried the whole way about the boat payment due at the end of the season. At thirty-six, I was a father of five, president of Old Harbor Native Corporation, and coming off my best commercial fishing season in over twenty years in the Kodiak fishery. My focus was on the future. Salmon prices hit a record high for Alaska in 1988. My recent seasonal catches left me confident that I had realized my dream of making a living at something I loved and could pass on to my kids if they chose a fisherman's life.

By the time I reached Kodiak in late April the herring season was cut short and already over because of oiled waters. Except for a few trawlers on charter with Exxon, the nation's largest fishing fleet was tied to the docks of St. Paul's Harbor. Kodiak's waterfront bars and restaurants were packed with anxious captains and crew eager to pick up where we left off in 1988.

En route from the Barren Islands to Kodiak, I had passed through oil slicks, sheen, and saw for the first time what became known as "mousse." It wasn't pretty. The floating brown globs were an alien presence in our pristine home waters. The prospect of retrieving a seine net without oiling the catch would be chancy. To do it all day long for a summer would be impossible. Mixing oiled fish with clean fish in the boat's hold would ruin a day's work. Canneries demand quality, fresh, clean fish or don't bother making a delivery. I agreed with those who said it would be better to miss a season than risk Kodiak's seafood reputation with oiled product. Exxon promised to "make everyone whole," and their spokesmen told the *Kodiak Daily Mirror* they'd "keep their Kodiak office open for twenty years if necessary to pay off legitimate claims of financial loss."

People were uneasy over the federal decision to turn the oil spill clean up over to Exxon. But no one had lived through the nation's worst environmental accident before. Why doubt the world's largest corporation with annual profits in excess of $5 billion at that time (now in excess of $8 billion) would not keep its promise?

Like most of the fleet, my sights were set on the May twenty-four-hour halibut opener, a deep water bottom fishery using hooks and longlines instead of seines. We wouldn't have the same oil contact risk and I could finally earn a payday with the new boat. Exxon and the Alaska Department of Fish and Game (ADF&G) said the salmon season might be delayed, but not canceled—maybe we'd catch fewer fish in a shortened season but higher prices would make up the difference.

The *Carla Rae C* performed well in the halibut opener, but we saw tarballs, sheen, mousse, and dead birds in the water. There were reports of submerged oil and oil on the bottom. What was worse, the waters around the village of Old Harbor were getting more oil from the south than the north. Beaches with southern tidal exposure were getting the most oil because the oil had gone down the Shelikof Strait, around Cape Trinity and up the east side of Kodiak Island to our area.

We'd always known Kodiak's location makes it a natural collector of the plankton biomass swirling in Gulf of Alaska currents. The plankton is drawn toward Kodiak's shores by currents, eddies, and winds and creates a nutrient rich marine ecosystem providing food for everything from candle fish to seabirds, and migrating salmon and whales. As with plankton, so with oil. Our capes, headlands, and islets became natural collectors of tarballs, mousse, and dead birds.

Given the much larger area to cover on Kodiak than the oiled area of Prince William Sound—and almost no clean-up crews—oil washed

The Kodiak water front (circa 1958) was demolished by the 1964 Good Friday earthquake and tsunami (Kodiak Historical Society).

ashore on beaches and then back into open water by tides and storms until being pushed ashore again somewhere else, always leaving greasy, oily residue behind. The slick's dispersal the experts hoped for early in the spill became an infuriating scenario for us with tarballs and mousse appearing randomly any place at any time. Submerged oil meant there were no safe havens. Tanner crab were caught in our subsistence pots with oil in their gills. The suddenness of the spill and needless wildlife death shocked us, but soon people adopted a "tough it out" attitude. Kodiak's people—especially villagers—live with stormy weather, natural disaster, and sudden tragic deaths. Commercial fishing is the nation's most hazardous job. It is common to lose friends and family members to the sea. Out of nine boys in my family, four have died at sea. The 1964 earthquake and tidal wave wiped out the village of Old Harbor with every building except the church and school destroyed. My most vivid childhood memory is standing on the hill above the village and seeing everyone's homes and possessions wash out to sea. During the 1964 earthquake, one person from Old

Harbor was killed and three died in the neighboring Kaguyak which also was leveled but never rebuilt, in contrast to Old Harbor.

As May became June, the salmon season was still on hold. Exxon still promised to "make us whole," but everyone's money was running out. A few people learned that they could obtain an Exxon clean up charter, but most of the fleet was waiting to fish. Exxon didn't offer to put the whole Kodiak fleet on charter as they had in Prince William Sound and soon gained a reputation for either denying, or nickel and diming, every request for assistance from the fleet.

People in the villages ran out of grocery money, and when they tried to gather subsistence foods they found oily carcasses on the beach. If oil was killing wildlife, could it kill us too? Health aides had no answers and simply urged people to use a smell test. "If it smells like oil, don't eat it."

An air of desperation set in and Kodiak experienced six suicides by June, including a thirty-year-old crewman who'd grown up in the village who simply walked off the end of the Old Harbor pier and drowned in broad daylight. Mental health cases shot up by 700 percent. Crewmen who could travel were bailing out to find work outside the spill region while they might have a chance to fish. Families were strained. A Kodiak woman murdered her husband.

I don't know how other people would react if their jobs and incomes were lost overnight due to an ecological disaster, but the prospect of watching most of the year's income disappear with the salmon closure created a volatile mix of anger and helplessness during our favorite and most productive time of the year. This anger often became rage when it was compounded by having to go begging to Exxon for any financial relief. When we were turned down, it made us double victims of this oil spill.

Boat payments, limited entry fishing permit payments, mortgages, and bills were depleting whatever savings people had. Those without savings sold hard earned assets like fishing permits—the basis of their future income—simply to feed their families that summer.

Finally, our worst fears came true. In August, Exxon and ADF&G dropped a bombshell we felt was coming and announced the cancellation of Kodiak's salmon season in all but a set-net-only district on the south end of the island. Perhaps to avoid a riot, Exxon finally increased the number of boats on oil clean-up charter. After villagers formed unauthorized beach clean-up crews, Exxon finally agreed to pay villagers at a lower rate than what they'd paid people in Prince William Sound. My Exxon charter earnings covered less than a tenth of a normal salmon season's income, but there was much worse to come.

In 1990, we had a salmon season, but our Japanese markets—which accounted for 90% of our sales—had collapsed. In 1989, a flood of farmed fish had filled Kodiak's salmon void. We've never recovered. Prices for Kodiak herring and salmon declined every year from the oil spill until last year, 1998. Over that decade salmon prices collapsed by almost 75%, with statewide earnings to fishermen falling by 75% from 1988 to 1998.

In addition to price collapses, the reduced Japanese market for Alaskan salmon put the fleet on "catch limits" so we couldn't make up with volume what we lost in price. The similar devaluation of limited entry fishing permits eroded our net worth. The Kodiak fleet experienced a flood of bankruptcies; forced sales of boats, permits, and marine equipment; IRS seizures; crew lay offs; increased welfare dependency; more suicides; and careers, families, and lives lost to drug and alcohol abuse. By the 1998 salmon season only 200 out of 380 Kodiak seine permits were fished.

Subsequent closures of the tanner crab fishery in the early 1990s and the imposition of Individual Fishing Quotas for halibut and black cod in the years since the spill made the collapse of the herring and salmon markets all the more devastating to our village fleet. A decade after the *Exxon Valdez* oil spill, a "good" commercial fishing season for the surviving small boat fleet is where you manage to pay the crew, keep your boat, and stave off bankruptcy for another year.

Exxon never made us "whole" and within weeks after they pulled out their clean-up operation in September, 40,000 commercial fishermen, subsistence users, and other spill-affected businesses and landowners in the spill region filed a class action lawsuit to recover damages. Five years later, in 1994, we won a $5.2 billion damage verdict in Federal Court in Anchorage. These funds could go a long way to "making us whole," but the money can't restore the lives altered, the bankruptcies, the marriages ruined, the children who suffered from the family stress and break-ups, or the general change for the worse in the way of life of rural, coastal Alaskans.

Exxon has fielded an army of attorneys and vowed to appeal all the way to the Supreme Court no matter how long it takes. In 1995, and in subsequent years, Exxon has lost motion after motion for retrial. The case is now pending in the 9th Circuit Court of Appeals and oral arguments were heard May 3, 1999. If Exxon fails again it is on to the Supreme Court. Exxon won't discuss settlement because they're making more off investing the $5 billion than they lose through the interest accumulating on the judgment. (Exxon's internal rate of return is 15 percent to 18 percent and the federal judgment rate is 5.9 percent.) It is hard, having lived through the spill and its aftermath, to understand how the board of directors of Exxon can live with themselves while condoning a "scorched earth" approach to the litigation. If there is a no equitable resolution or settlement of some kind, this wound will fester for eternity.

THE LARGEST ENVIRONMENTAL FINE IN U.S. HISTORY

The class action suit wasn't the only trial Exxon faced as a result of the oil spill. In August 1989, the State of Alaska filed suit against Exxon alleging negligence for failing to prevent, and clean up, the spill. Thereafter, in October 1991, the state and federal suits were combined and after lengthy negotiations a landmark $1 billion criminal and civil settlement was reached with Exxon. The funds would be paid out over a ten-year period and would be controlled by a six-member joint state and federal trustee council to "restore and enhance the oil spill impacted wildlife in the 1,400 mile oil spill region."

Although the $1 billion Exxon settlement with the state and federal government would not compensate fishermen, individuals, land-owners, or private companies that had suffered losses, it created a potential opportunity for private land-owners in the region to generate economic activity from their lands.

Under the 1971 Alaska Native Claims Settlement Act (ANCSA), the Kodiak and Afognak Native corporations had selected the best salmon rivers and developable coastal areas in the Kodiak Archipelago. These rivers produced more than 70 percent of Kodiak's annual salmon return.

While Native corporations didn't own the fish, we owned the critical spawning habitat needed for all future runs, and as a result of congressional action, our future economic development of these lands put us on a collision course with maintaining pristine salmon habitat.

The Department of Interior in an earlier report on Kodiak Island stated:

> "Native corporation lands represent the most biologically productive river systems and coastal habitats on the island. Perhaps as important, they constitute a major component of a larger ecosystem that must be preserved intact to assure the continued viability of the Kodiak brown bear. The challenge to the integrity of this ecosystem could come on several fronts."

To grasp the severity of the threats the Department of Interior feared, it's necessary to understand ANCSA's impact on Kodiak's land ownership. ANCSA represents the fulfillment of the agreement made by Congress in the 1867 Treaty of Purchase of Alaska from Russia. As subjects of the Czar, the Russian Orthodox church insisted that we retain inalienable rights to our traditional hunting and fishing areas. It seemed like a small condition and compatible with U.S. policy toward Native Americans. If Alaska hadn't been purchased, it likely would have ended up as part of Canada.

In 1971, Congress sought to resolve these aboriginal land claims in order to build the Alaska pipeline, except ANCSA's corporate model would be substituted for the Bureau of Indian Affairs (BIA) reservation system in the Lower 48 states. ANCSA provided a one-time infusion of money and large-scale conveyance of federal land to set up village and regional corporations making every qualified Native alive in 1971 a shareholder. Shareholder returns would come from the corporations' investment of money and land development, not the federal taxpayer.

Native land selections proved very valuable in some cases. Corporations with major oil and gas reserves like Arctic Slope Regional Corp., or commercial timber such as Sealaska, or prime real estate like Cook Inlet Regional, Inc., thrived under ANCSA and are among the largest Alaska corporations.

Old Harbor Native Corporation, on the other hand, was forced by ANCSA to select a substantial portion of its lands inside the Kodiak

NWR where there are no commercially developable oil, timber, or other known mineral resources. The only viable economic option available to us was to subdivide our real estate for recreational, resort, or tourism development or other uses of the land—some not conducive to the best use of most of it generally—as wildlife habitat.

At the time ANCSA passed, Congress understood they were creating a problem for the Kodiak NWR. If we developed our refuge inholdings, the brown bear and salmon habitat would be ruined. If we left them undeveloped, the bears and salmon would be fine, but our shareholders would receive no direct economic benefit from ANCSA.

Alaska's Natives had waited 104 years since the 1867 purchase of Alaska from Russia to have their traditional lands granted back under the power of American law. ANCSA passed with Section 22(g) in the bill which attempted to restrict "incompatible" uses of land selected inside National Wildlife Refuges. The provision was viewed by Natives as an attempt at "giving something with one hand and taking with the other." By the mid-1980s the clock was ticking on the potential for incompatible economic development in the Kodiak NWR. Would Section 22(g) hold up to a legal challenge if Native corporations seriously pursued development? No one knew. The Department of Interior and the Native corporations began exploring the possibility of the United States acquiring the inholdings in the 1980s. That was the status quo when the *Exxon Valdez* ran aground at Bligh Reef in Prince William Sound.

One phenomenon from oil spill summer that intrigued us was the flood of outside visitors—particularly federal officials, members of Congress, congressional staffers, and media—to Kodiak Island and even the Native villages. It became normal that summer to have a television film crew in the village in the morning and a group of congressmen in the afternoon and a newspaper reporter for dinner.

This was a predictable side effect of the intense national interest in the oil spill, but it was an entirely new experience for us. We recognized that it provided us an extraordinary platform on which to discuss the dilemma of the corporation's bear refuge inholdings.

We answered their question about the spill's impact—"Yes the oil spill was a disaster, but if the Department of Interior doesn't work out something with us on the refuge inholdings, you are probably one of the last people to see the Kodiak bear refuge as it was envisioned when established by President Roosevelt." We found that our visitors were persuaded of the injustice Kodiak Native corporations suffered under Section 22(g).

Repeatedly our visitors would ask, "You mean you were provided land in settlement of your aboriginal claims that the government claims you can't do anything with?" Yes. Or, "If you develop the land, the bears lose out?" Yes. Gradually the so-called "Bear habitat-Native lands" dilemma on Kodiak Island found a constituency. Our discussions caught the imagination and concern of visitors and the dimensions of the problem began to become clear.

The Native corporation inholding dilemma could get dramatically worse and destroy the integrity of the Kodiak bear refuge. We knew it, the Department of Interior knew it, and many from Washington, D.C., Juneau, and the media were learning it. We were able to get our problem before the public like never before, and with a force that we never imagined because the issue was real and vital to a biologically rich area of our country.

FINDING OUR VOICE

As winter arrived, the community remained in shock from the oil spill, but we were glad the tide of visitors left us alone. Our common hardships brought out a togetherness and cooperation that had disappeared that summer. People were helping each other put up fish. Deer and duck hunting parties worked to fill the food reserves for every family. Elders received the care and attention they deserved.

From the Native corporation's point of view, we faced uncertainty but our attitude began to shift as 1990 began. We'd taken a hard shot economically but we'd found our voice. The consensus among many Alaskan politicians was cautiously optimistic. "Something would be done." The Department of Interior was sending positive signals. The members of the Alaska congressional delegation were insisting on fairness for Alaskans. The local Native corporations adopted an outreach campaign on the first anniversary of the oil spill with the objective of focusing on the inholding dilemma.

The economy of Kodiak Island improved as the fishing fleet had a spring herring season and a summer of salmon fishing. Although salmon prices paid to fishermen had fallen 30 percent from 1988, the fleet was at least working.

By coincidence, 1991 was the fiftith anniversary of the founding of the Kodiak NWR by President Franklin Roosevelt and the growing necessity to develop or do something with inholdings in prime brown bear habitat gained the attention of television, magazine, and newspaper editors. The *Anchorage Times* did a Sunday page one feature story on the fate of Kodiak's bears and the World Wildlife Fund, the world's largest environmental group, made Kodiak one of its top North America conservation issues.

In response to a *Newsweek* story, Congressman Don Young wrote a letter to the editor championing the cause and portraying the issue exactly as it was:

> "The benefits to Natives and conservation from reacquisition of Native inholdings in our Alaska lands is an issue that deserved Congressional support on its own merits. We have here people among the most deprived in the Nation, who want to convert their only asset into economically beneficial investments to better their lot and reduce their dependence on Kodiak Refuge resources. And we have a fragile ecosystem for the World's largest and most majestic carnivore. With federal acquisition, the cause of conservation and the Natives both win."

Congressman Young made it clear in a letter to the *Anchorage Daily News* that he didn't normally support such acquisition of private lands unless it makes good sense and that in the case of the lands on Kodiak it did. He deserves credit for supporting the opening of these lands to hunters, sport fishermen, and other outdoorsmen and women. (Also, Alaska Senator Ted Stevens obtained the first funding to conserve, thereby helping to protect the refuge as Presidents Roosevelt and Eisenhower sought to do.)

The debate over Section 22(g) heated up in 1991 as well. The U.S. Fish and Wildlife Service regional director issued a memo to clarify just what Section 22(g) meant in terms of enforceable restrictions the government held over our lands. He concluded that 22(g) appeared weak,

"Written and oral legal advice throughout the years since 1971 has been that regulations specific to the 22(g) lands must be promulgated to implement. . . . Such regulations have not been issued and are not currently under development. Because this issue is so unsettled, we need to work with the landowners, rather than try to regulate them, to conserve fish and wildlife resources as best we can." The government was wisely choosing to work with the landowners in an attempt to develop a reasonable solution to this issue.

In October 1991, the joint state and federal negotiating team, led by Alaska Attorney General Charlie Cole, reached a $1 billion settlement that resolved criminal charges and civil claims of the United States and the State of Alaska against Exxon for recovery of damages caused by the oil spill. Under the personal insistence of Governor Hickel, the state and federal government would not settle for less than $1 billion, and they got it, setting a record for the highest recovery for an environmental disaster in the nation's history. The Memorandum of Agreement with Exxon created a six-member state and federal Trustee Council to allocate the

Threats to Kodiak's bears alarmed all who learned of the
Native inholding dilemma (George Mobley).

money, and provided rules for spending the remaining dollars after deducting expenses for cleanup activities. Those rules were:

- Restoration funds must be used ". . . for the purposes of restoring, replacing, enhancing, or acquiring the equivalent of natural resources injured as a result of the Oil Spill and the reduced or lost services provided by such resources . . . ."
- Restoration funds must be spent on restoration of natural resources in Alaska unless the Trustees unanimously agree that spending funds outside of the state is necessary for effective restoration.
- All decisions made by the Trustees (such as spending restoration funds) must be made by unanimous consent.

Unfortunately, the Exxon settlement was only for "damages to publicly owned natural resources affected by the spill," and the settlement did not cover claims from private parties, including—and especially—commercial fishermen, subsistence users, and Alaska Native corporations (which own nearly all the private land in the spill area).

Spending money to acquire Native corporations' inholdings in the Kodiak refuge, in the Chugach National Forest in Prince William Sound, and within the Kenai Fiords National Park and Kachemak Bay State Park qualified under the first rule, ". . . for the purposes of restoring, replacing, enhancing, or acquiring the equivalent of natural resources injured as a result of the Oil Spill."

However, there was no court mandated provision in the settlement that bound the Trustee Council to do that. Whatever funds Native corporations might receive in the future would require a unanimous six votes from the Trustee Council. It meant that federal and state agencies had to cooperate with one other—something rarely seen.

Media interest in Kodiak accelerated in 1992, with *National Geographic* magazine and film crews in the field that summer examining the whole island with special emphasis on the "bear habitat-Native lands" dilemma. *Time* and *The Washington Post* did stories updating the whole oil spill region status while CNN TV and radio covered Kodiak again as

Environmental leaders on the Ayakulik River. From left (seated)
Dave Cline, National Audubon Society; (standing) Jack Hession, Sierra Club;
Chuck Clusen, Natural Resources Defense Council; Don Barry,
World Wildlife Fund; (seated) Doug Miller, National Wildlife Federation;
Pam Miller, Wilderness Society (Tim Richardson).

did National Public Radio, the *London Times,* the *Pittsburgh Press,* the *Seattle Times* and the *London Daily Mail.*

The Kodiak commercial salmon industry weighed into the debate on the side of habitat conservation through acquiring Native corporation lands, spokesman Larry Malloy told the *Mirror,* "In terms of the habitat issue, I think federal reacquisition in the refuge is extremely important. Wherever you can retain habitat as pristine as possible you know you're looking after the stability of salmon production."

That December Kodiak refuge inholdings made the USFWS' priority list for Land and Water Conservation Fund (LWCF) monies. The LWCF program uses federal oil and gas royalties from outer continental shelf drilling to buy critical habitat parcels inside the nation's parks, forests, and refuges.

It was hard to believe, but at the beginning of 1993, it was nearly four years since the spill, there had been little restoration actually done, no benefits going back to the people, and wildlife injured by the spill. A hard-nosed and sometimes bitter realism often develops among Native leaders when confronted with government's maze of complexity, and decades of broken promises from Washington, D.C. It took Congress 104 years to spell out the Native land claims agreed to in 1867. The bottom line is that Native American issues are oftentimes way down the list of federal and state priorities. In an era of budgetary austerity would Kodiak's "bear habitat-Native lands" dilemma really matter? Would our issues and problems compete with defense spending, highway spending, Medicare, and so on?

Although we'd received support and sympathy from many people, there was no transaction achieved yet. My responsibility as corporation president was to seek to achieve the economic, cultural, and social benefit to the shareholders as envisioned by ANCSA, while at the same time conserving the land for subsistence and other traditional uses by the village residents.

Although our losses and problems had received good visibility, it became apparent that trying to actually achieve a fair return for our shareholders, yet protect the lands that were special to us, we needed help to get the combined federal and state government to work with us. Consequently, we assembled a team of advisors and advocates with years of experience to help us achieve our goals.

We recognized that we could not focus only on Old Harbor but rather needed to make sure there was a larger commitment to protection of habitat and inholdings in the entire spill region. Consequently, we had to be sensitive to the needs of Prince William Sound as well as other parts of Kodiak and Afognak Islands.

On the fourth anniversary of the oil spill, March 24, 1993, the Clinton administration announced that $25 million of the federal criminal funds would be spent on habitat protection and named Kodiak refuge inholdings as one of the areas under consideration. The *Anchorage Daily News* reacted favorably to the administration's move: "Add to the proposed federal purchases Governor Wally Hickel's plan to buy land and complete Kachemak Bay State Park, and you have the start of something good: a higher level of protection for one of the most ecologically rich and beautiful coastlines in the world."

At the beginning of April, the *Exxon Valdez* Oil Spill (EVOS) Trustee Council put out a draft restoration plan which sought public comment on a variety of restoration options, from habitat protection to monitoring and research. Habitat protection at varying dollar commitments was in each of the five alternatives put forward for public comment. There was a commitment to protecting habitat and the EVOS process appeared to be moving.

Although our interest in land acquisition had always focused on our Kodiak NWR inholdings, the biological assessment team for the EVOS Trustee Council made a surprise announcement early in 1993. They considered our old-growth timbered lands on northeast Afognak Island as imminently threatened by logging and should therefore be negotiated for by the Trustee Council immediately, even before an overall plan for the region was adopted.

Our Afognak lands at Seal Bay were threatened because our logging joint venture known as Seal Bay Timber Company was ready to commence our second year of harvesting.

This fact alarmed the environmental community, especially the Alaska Rainforest Campaign, which brought pressure to bear on the EVOS Trustee Council to rapidly negotiate a habitat protection sale from us. We, along with our joint venture partner Akhiok Kaguyak, Inc., agreed to be willing sellers if we could obtain fair market value for the timber. But we could not delay logging operations because the timber market was surging and our shareholders deserved some dividends from their ANCSA corporation. We had an ongoing fiduciary responsibility to our shareholders. Harvesting the trees was one way to generate economic benefit to shareholders. Another was to conserve the trees. For us it made sense to consider selling a conservation easement to protect the trees, then put most of the proceeds in a trust fund to benefit shareholders.

Since land protected on Afognak would go to the Alaska State Park System, Attorney General Cole led the negotiations for the Trustee Council. Our negotiating team was in touch with the Old Harbor Board of Directors and me on a daily basis as the Seal Bay negotiations progressed.

May began without an agreement in sight. A *Kodiak Daily Mirror* headline captured the tension: "Negotiators race chain saws for Seal Bay timber." We were willing to try to negotiate a habitat conservation/ restoration agreement, but the timber market was near an all-time high. There was public interest in the EVOS Trustee Council negotiating its first stand-alone habitat purchase. The Kachemak habitat conservation effort that succeeded in March had been twenty years in the making and utilized state legislative funds, Alyeska funds and the state's criminal settlement.

The Seal Bay transaction came up very quickly in terms of issues' education by our negotiators. At what both sides agreed was the last minute, a meeting was called in Anchorage in early May with the full Trustee Council. The transaction unfolded in public right before about fifty people who attended the Trustees' meeting Thursday, and many other telephone and radio hook-ups the Council uses for the benefit of the public. If ever there was a "public" process, this was it . . . right before the eyes of the world. After hours of discussions, the Trustee Council offered to buy approximately 42,000 acres at $38.7 million which included 17,400 at Seal Bay and 25,000 acres of pristine forested land on Tonki Cape.

The agreement was adopted. It was a win of which we were proud . . . the public and our corporation and our partner in Seal Bay, Akhiok Kaguyak, Inc., all won out that day.

The Seal Bay purchase was national news with the *New York Times, Wall Street Journal,* the *Washington Post,* and CNN providing coverage. The reaction to Seal Bay underscored that the refuge inholding transaction would also be a clear win for the Kodiak and Alaska economy, not simply conservation, oil spill injured wildlife, and the bears. The Kodiak Chamber of Commerce, the Kodiak salmon industry leaders, the commercial fishery industry—all saw this for what it was—a major win for the future economic vitality of the Kodiak area. Kodiak's tourism industry, its sport hunting and fishing community, also were supportive.

In June, the National Rifle Association, Safari Club International, and Wildlife Legislative Fund of America sent a letter to the Trustees that was echoed by other sportsmen's groups. The letter stated, "We support acquisition of critical brown bear, bald eagle, anadromous fish, marine mammal, and seabird habitat on Native corporation inholdings in the

Kodiak NWR and adjacent lands. Such acquisitions would meet four restoration objectives which we endorse:

- Provide greater public access to lands now closed to such access for both consumptive and non-consumptive uses;
- Consolidate the management of the bear refuge and salmon streams by the U.S. Fish and Wildlife Service and the Alaska Department of Fish & Game;
- Conserve in perpetuity Kodiak brown bear and other wildlife habitats; and
- Stimulate economic growth, including hunting and related tourism, in areas where such growth should take place for the benefit of Natives and non-Natives alike.

"Just as sportsmen led the effort to persuade President Franklin D. Roosevelt to create the refuge in 1941, we support your efforts to make it whole."

INTERIOR SECRETARY BABBITT PAYS A VISIT

In August, Assistant Secretary of Interior Frampton told the Associated Press, "Our biggest priority is to get the *Exxon Valdez* trust funds on track. There is an opportunity to leave a tremendous legacy in terms of ecosystem restoration . . ." and Interior Secretary Bruce Babbitt paid a visit to Kodiak and Old Harbor to see first-hand the habitat in question in the Kodiak refuge.

The excitement level in our community was high when Secretary Babbitt visited. Almost the whole village went to the airstrip to meet the planes carrying him and others traveling with him. The secretary walked through our village and we talked about what was occurring. The walk ended at our Russian Orthodox Church.

During our conversation, the secretary said he had never been commercial fishing. I offered to show him since that's what we do in Old Harbor as a mainstay of our economy there. Secretary Babbitt changed his schedule to enable him to go commercial fishing, and the next morning the float plane flew in and dropped the secretary off at my boat. During the time we spent together drinking coffee and talking, we were able to catch some salmon, observe a school of killer whales swimming by, and I was able to talk to Secretary Babbitt about my people and my village. It also gave me a chance to show him how generations of our people have made their living and why our culture and the culture of our ancestors evolved around the sea.

Secretary Babbitt, in a statement later that day at Three Saints Bay, the site of the first Russian settlement in Alaska, talked about the importance of our community and recognized that these islands may represent the most important totally intact ecosystem in the United States.

The results of the public comments on the EVOS Restoration Plan were published that September. They showed that the public wanted 66 percent of the funds to be used to purchase land to conserve habitat and 30 percent used for marine research.

The November *National Geographic* magazine came out in late October with a photo of Old Harbor as the lead picture. The dramatic story on Kodiak began from the deck of my brother Jack's fishing boat and went on to detail the Native inholding dilemma the way only that magazine can. Underscoring the dangers I mentioned earlier about the fishing industry which had been my family's livelihood, Jack lost his life to the sea in an accident three years later.

The patience required to accomplish something as important as this land transaction, and to control your own frustration, becomes a life-changing process. It's hard on families as well as oneself. It's not something I sought, but my urge to throw up my hands and quit the whole mess was countered by a stronger urge to make something positive happen for my people out of the *Exxon Valdez* disaster.

On November 5th, the State of Alaska Legislative Budget and Audit committee approved the Seal Bay transaction. The EVOS Trustee Council had accomplished its first stand-alone acquisition.

On November 30th, the EVOS Trustee Council unveiled their region-wide habitat parcel ranking list totaling 850,000 acres. In order for the land parcels to make the EVOS list, they had to be offered by a willing seller and contain habitat important to oil spill injured resources or services. The resources the biologists used to compile the parcel ranking had been identified over three years of damage assessment as having been negatively impacted by the oil spill. The injured resources list included pink and sockeye salmon, Dolly Varden and cutthroat trout, herring, bald eagle, black oystercatcher, common murre, harbor seal, harlequin duck, marbled murrelet, pigeon guillemot, river otter, sea otter, intertidal organisms, and archaeological sites. Human services that qualified in the habitat protection rankings included rural subsistence, recreation, and tourism.

Parcels that had the optimum combination of these resources and services ranked higher on the priority list than parcels with fewer of these resources and services or with lower quality and quantity of these resources and services. When the rankings came out, Kodiak Archipelago lands represented 75 percent of the highest ranking acreage in the entire oil spill region.

The good news in November 1993 was capped off by Trustee Council approval of $1.5 million for the construction of an artifact repository sponsored by the Kodiak Area Native Association, which today is known as the Alutiiq Museum and Repository and represents one of the finest Native Alaskan cultural centers in the state.

Preliminary negotiations over our refuge inholdings began with a Trustee Council negotiating team in 1994. We entered the fifth year after the oil spill with a degree of confidence that a comprehensive Kodiak NWR refuge habitat package was achievable. We knew our success depended on the support of many different quarters. Among support groups were the Kodiak commercial salmon industry, sportsmen, and conservationists.

Although we were fresh off completing the Seal Bay acquisition and the Kodiak refuge inholdings ranked at the top of the EVOS priority list, it was already nearly five years after the oil spill. We were after all, for the most part, commercial fishermen, not seasoned political infighters who'd asked for this kind of effort by choice. However, we forged ahead with the support of the board of directors and the shareholders.

In early 1994, the release of *National Geographic's* film *Island of the Giant Bears* occurred in Washington, D.C. The film is a visually stunning depiction of Kodiak Island and presents a forceful explanation of the inholding dilemma. We felt honored to have been subjects of the film. While there had been many articles in *Time, Newsweek, National Geographic,* and all the nation's leading newspapers, none of that coverage had the emotional impact on us the Geographic's film did nor did they reach hundreds of millions of people in eighty countries around the world as this film would.

The head of *National Geographic,* Gilbert Grosvenor, concluded his remarks at the premier stating, "The tale of the Kodiak bear is a story in a microcosm of our continued need to protect the earth's precious resources. . . . At the same time we must also fulfill legitimate human needs and allow for economic growth and prosperity ". . . .

From Mr. Grosvenor's comments we entered a nine-month period of intense discussions with the federal government over the fair market value of our lands. The fundamental issue involves how to affix monetary value to unique wild lands, wetlands, bird rookeries, and marine environments where commercial development has either not been attempted to date, or where there are few comparable sales to guide appraisers.

REACHING CONSENSUS & CLOSING THE DEAL

The fifth anniversary of the *Exxon Valdez* oil spill, March 24, 1994, brought about a time for reflection and a renewed commitment by everyone in the EVOS process to get the restoration job done. The EVOS Trustee Council had not yet completed their restoration plan, but they were close. On March 27th, the *Anchorage Daily News* captured what we and many participants were feeling in an editorial. Stating that the Trustee Council was close to approving their comprehensive, regionally balanced restoration plan, the *News* wrote:

"Granted the plan isn't going to please everybody. This being Alaska, passions run high over how the money should—and should not—be spent. . . . Not all the problems from the spill can be solved, unfortunately. . . . But some good can come from the settlement. Environmentalists may get only half the money they want for habitat, but the lands the trustee council ranks as its top priorities would be well worth protecting. These include Native inholdings in the Kodiak National Wildlife

Refuge and Kenai Fjords National Park. and various parcels in Prince William Sound. The landowners are willing sellers. And the acquisitions would be . . . scientific and economic investments, since protecting critical habitat is key to keeping the North Pacific diverse and productive."

Two days later, the *News* commented again on the Kodiak habitat acquisitions in a second editorial:

"The Kodiak . . . (habitat conservation effort) is a no-lose proposal. . . . Using some of the oil spill settlement to protect this extraordinary habitat would be a fitting settlement to the state's worst environmental accident."

In June, Congressmen Don Young and George Miller wrote a joint Dear Colleague letter announcing the airing of *National Geographic's* Kodiak film on the House of Representative's cable system. The two members of Congress, who are on many occasions on opposite sides of issues, found themselves both supporting the Kodiak habitat conservation effort and stated: "As illustrated by the film, the benefits resulting from this comprehensive effort include, (1) mitigation of some of the injuries resulting from the *Exxon Valdez* oil spill; (2) increased access to inholdings which are now closed to the public; (3) conservation of stream beds, weir sites, and wildlife habitat which are essential to the commercial fishing, sport fishing, hunting, and recreation industries; (4) improving the long-range viability of the rural Alaskan way of life; (5) enhanced management of fish and game and their habitat by the State of Alaska and the U.S. Fish and Wildlife Service; and (6) stimulation of economic activity in the region."

For our part, we left the day-to-day negotiations to the consulting team throughout 1994 and we tried to finish up the fourth disappointing salmon season since the spill.

Finally in May of 1995, we were able to reach an agreement with the Trustee Council and signed the formal documents culminating this long effort begun a decade before to conserve this habitat and to help our corporation fulfill its role as envisioned in ANCSA.

As I reflect back on our land acquisition experience of trying to meet the fiduciary responsibility to provide a return to our shareholders while

*Interior Secretary Bruce Babbitt (left in Alutiiq kayaker's hat) and Old Harbor
Native Corporation President Emil Christiansen sign the first large-scale Kodiak
NWR habitat protection agreements, May 1995 (Tim Richardson).*

protecting our culture and honoring a personal responsibility to protect
the land, I recognize that we learned many lessons.

A key to this achievement was a high level of cooperation that developed between our Native village corporation, and our sister Native
corporation to the south, Akhiok Kaguyak, Inc. Their president, Ralph
Eluska, and their board of directors, worked with us very closely in an effort to achieve a lasting legacy for the shareholders of both corporations.

You need great patience and persistence to keep going. The ultimate
success of this effort was attributable to many decisions, especially to
those by our corporation's board of directors and by our shareholders.
This is not easy sledding. If it was, people would have gotten through it
in a few months. That did not happen. This process literally took years.

In the vast and impersonal government arena, it was important for
us that there be people who would be fair in dealing with us, and fortunately for us there were such people involved who tried to balance equitably the public's interest and that of the landowner.

The end result provided for conserving many thousands of acres of habitat lands in perpetuity, opening those lands to the public for hunting, fishing, and outdoor recreation, and providing short and long term economic benefits for our people.

It was a good result for all sides…and one well worth the extraordinary effort it took to achieve.

OUR ANGER HAS NO PLACE TO GO

We are living within a window of opportunity of Exxon.
Mother Nature lives within the same window.
She has no lawyers, no money, only evidence of death and destruction.
She has hidden nothing and requested little.
I look to my children's eyes for strength, continually searching for answers.
Afraid of the truth but afraid more for our future.
I can't run. I can't sleep in this silence. I am consumed by this oil, not by
　　　　choice.
I was born of this land, these waters.
I've ingested the food, the wisdom, the peace.
I am suffocating and gasping for breath.
I look to my grandfather, my grandmother,
　　　　buried on the hill above the village of old Karluk.
I look to my ancestors buried in this graveyard.
I look for the strength to endure this.
The birds don't sing any more.
The whales don't dance on the ocean.
Baby sea otters looking for their mothers.
Morning breeze brings smells of death.
Night brings still more silence.
My heart beats fast each day.
Exxon's departure approaches.
Will they leave us to bury our dead,
　　　　to feed our children?
Look for a bird, a whale, a bear, a deer, anything to signify life.
We have been beaten, demoralized,
　　　　reduced to beggars seeking a parcel of bread to feed our children.
Join us at our table of mourning.
I pray to my ancestors who have gone before me
　　　　and look to God to find the words to define our losses.
The dead count on Kodiak is three to four times that of Prince William
　　　　Sound.

Though we are continuously assured the oil continues to weather,
  we pick up carcasses by the thousands.
No one knows for certain the oil is non-toxic.
No one has the expertise.
We are guinea pigs in a giant experiment.
Facts made to fit the hypothesis.
From time immemorial,
  Aleuts and native people of this island
  have made their livelihood from this water and land.
Experts in catching salmon, hunting,
  respect for Mother Nature.
Sharing the bounty with needy others.
Today we fish for oil instead of fish.
The removal of a way of life.
The highest price short of death.
Our past exposed.
Our present uprooted.
Our future at the mercy of Exxon.

—DOLLY REFT
August 1989

Dolly Reft was born and raised in Kodiak, Alaska. Her grandfather was the last traditional chief of the native village of Karluk. The poem "Our Anger Has No Place to Go" was delivered at the August 8, 1989 public meeting of the Exxon Valdez Oil Spill Commission in Kodiak.

"An important concept to keep in mind is that we shouldn't be satisfied in the knowledge that Kodiak bears are merely present. We need to know that bears can be found on top of the highest ridges as well as along ocean beaches, that congregations of more than 100 animals still occur along only a mile of two of some streams, and that the landscape is still traversed by giant animals."

—*VICTOR G. BARNES, JR.*

Victor G. Barnes, Jr. was born and raised in Colorado, the starting point for a thirty-two-year career that would make him the world's foremost expert on the Kodiak brown bear.

Vic's first field work as a graduate student involved a study of black bears in Yellowstone National Park—their range, activity patterns, and interactions with people. Vic joined the U.S. Fish and Wildlife Service, and spent three years in Olympia, Washington, and twelve years in Bend, Oregon, where he studied forest mammals.

In 1982 he arrived on Kodiak as leader of the U.S. Department of Interior's Kodiak Brown Bear Research Project. For seventeen years Vic conducted such field research as population surveys and radio-collaring projects to understand bear movements, range, reproduction, and mortality.

While stationed in Alaska, Vic also served on bear research teams dealing with grizzly bears in Denali National Park and polar bears along Alaska's arctic northwest coast. Now retired and back in Colorado, Vic remains active as a consultant. His work provides important data for the long-term challenges of managing bears and people in the Kodiak NWR.

Ursus arctos middendorffi *Kodiak brown bear, (USFWS).*

CHAPTER 3

THE MAJESTIC KODIAK BROWN BEAR

VICTOR G. BARNES, JR.

The brown bears that roam the Kodiak Archipelago are one of the most widely recognized animal populations in the world. Their enormous size is legendary and they occur in densities that define optimum bear habitat. Each year more and more people visit Kodiak to photograph, hunt, or simply view these great animals. And they all want to learn more about Kodiak bears and what makes them so special.

Our best evidence indicates that Kodiak bears have been a distinct population since the retreat of glaciers about 12,000 years ago. We can only speculate on how the first animals arrived. It is unlikely that a land bridge ever extended southward from the Kenai Peninsula, but bears certainly could have reached Kodiak via shorefast ice and icefloes. They probably first migrated to the "Refugium," that portion of southwest Kodiak Island that was not glaciated during the last ice age. From there they spread northward as the glaciers retreated.

Kodiak bears have been separated from the mainland and other bear populations for thousands of years and this isolation is reflected in both physical characteristics and their genetic makeup. Studies of skull measurements led scientists to conclude that Kodiak bears were enough different from other bear populations to distinguish them as a subspecies. Thus, Kodiak bears are classed as *Ursus arctos middendorffi* while all other North American brown/grizzly bears have the scientific name of *Ursus arctos horribilis.*

Recently, other scientists discovered that Kodiak bears, because they have been isolated so long, have the least genetic variability of any brown bear population studied to date. In many animal populations, and cheetahs are a classic example, this lack of genetic diversity would be cause for concern. Because all signs point to a healthy bear population on

*Author Vic Barnes (right) and ADF & G's Roger Smith measure mature
Kodiak boar (Marion Owen).*

Kodiak, this new finding has scientists rethinking the role of genetic variation in bears.

Humans and bears have coexisted on the Kodiak Archipelago at least 7,000 years. Early Native people lived, fished, and hunted near the sea and probably devoted little time to the pursuit of bears. Nevertheless, bears were used to some extent for both food and fur. As with many Native cultures, bears on Kodiak undoubtedly were feared by some and revered by others. One thing we can be certain of is that Kodiak bears captured the imagination of Native people and, as today, were the subject of countless tales.

Little is known about the status of bears in the Kodiak area during the late 1700s, when Russian fur traders first arrived, and during the 1800s.

Historical accounts from the early 1900s, though, point to excessive killing of bears, at least in some locales. We know that the animals were hunted commercially for their hides before the sale of hides was banned in 1925. Also, indiscriminate killing of bears was common in the early 1900s because they were viewed as competitors by ranchers and commercial fisherman. Furthermore, sport hunting regulations were liberal—during 1925––1927 the bag limit was three bears with no season limitation.

MANAGING THE ISLAND OF THE GIANT BEARS

Concern for the welfare of the Kodiak bear escalated in the 1930s and ultimately led to establishment of the Kodiak NWR in 1941. Even with that important conservation step, Kodiak bears have endured some tough times. Trophy hunting was limited prior to World War II but rapidly increased after the war and was in full swing by 1950. Restrictions on season length and area closures were necessary in the 1960s to curtail excessive harvest of bears. This high sport harvest was compounded by a controversial bear control program on northeast Kodiak Island. That

Management of Kodiak bears has been aided by a strong commitment to research (Marion Owen).

project, which involved aerial gunning of bears, was undertaken to reduce bear depredations on livestock but was most effective in raising the ire of conservationists and drawing attention to the need for improved bear management. In the 1970s the sport harvest again rose sharply in some popular hunting spots and provided impetus for developing the area permit system that is still in effect.

Management of Kodiak bears is a responsibility shared by the Alaska Department of Fish and Game (ADF&G) and the U. S. Fish and Wildlife Service (USFWS). The ADF&G is primarily responsible for population management while USFWS focuses on habitat protection. Through cooperative projects and agreements the agencies assist each other in the two primary areas of responsibility. The goal of both agencies is to maintain density, distribution, and habitat-use patterns of bears at present levels. This is no small task. As commercial and private use continue to grow throughout the Kodiak region, bear managers must be constantly alert to changes in the bear population as well as new developments in human use of important or critical bear habitat.

Protection of habitat, and especially quality of that habitat, is the key to maintaining healthy wildlife populations. The bears on Kodiak have evolved on a landscape of remarkable diversity and one that has been largely in a wilderness state. Land acquisition efforts in recent years have made unprecedented progress towards maintaining the quality of that habitat. Returning Native-conveyed lands and other private parcels back into public ownership, in the form of either federal or state lands, is a huge step towards a bright future for Kodiak bears.

Another key component of habitat protection is managing the people that use Kodiak's public lands. It's important that people have an opportunity to enjoy these wildlands and their wildlife. It's equally important that this use have little or no long-term effect on how bears use the land. That is why it is so important to learn where and why bears use certain areas, how those patterns change from one season to the next, and how bears vary those patterns from year to year with the inevitable fluctuation in weather and other factors. Later in this chapter we will see how a rich history of research has shed new light on Kodiak bears and how they adapt to the changing moods of their environment.

Population management and habitat management go hand in hand. Even with good habitat, managers know that it is essential to keep bear mortality in check. In 1976 the ADF&G instituted an area permit system that distributed hunting equitably throughout the Kodiak Archipelago. Since that time this system has evolved into what is probably the most intensively managed bear hunt in Alaska. Since 1980 the annual harvest has averaged just over 160 animals.

All bears harvested in the Kodiak area must be sealed by ADF&G representatives. The sealing process provides data on sex, age, and skull size of all animals killed. These data, which are available from 1950 to date, provide a valuable record of harvest patterns over the years. Limited fluctuation in annual harvests since 1980 is encouraging evidence that the bear population is doing well. Over this period males have comprised about 65 percent of the harvest, including several boars each year that qualify for listing in Safari Club International or Boone and Crockett trophy lists. A thirteen-year-old boar taken in 1997 currently is tied for the number one spot in Safari Club records.

Even though sport harvest records indicate a healthy population, bear managers have not been complacent. In the mid 1990s, when research information indicated that sport harvest on some areas of southwest Kodiak was exceeding the desired limit, a new regulation was implemented that gives additional protection to females. This new system, which is based on skull measurements and penalizes the taking of females on guided hunts, appears to be having the desired effect.

Over the years management of Kodiak bears has consistently improved and this progress has been greatly aided by a strong commitment to research. Early efforts in the 1950s were directed at food habits, salmon-bear relationships, and the development of capture and marking techniques. Later, projects tackled a wide range of topics including reproduction, seasonal movements, alpine feeding, winter denning, density estimates, aerial survey techniques, and the effects of bear viewing. Gradually and collectively these projects have not only expanded our knowledge of these great animals, but also elevated our respect and admiration for them. Not surprisingly, each study shed new light and at the same time revealed how much more there is to learn.

One of the most frequently-asked questions about Kodiak bears is, "how big are they?" Kodiak bears, like all bears, start out very small. At birth they might not weigh much more than a pound. After that growth is rapid. By midsummer, when cubs are 6–7 months old, they will average about 50 pounds. At 3 1/2 years, when young bears are on their own and called subadults, they will average about 300 pounds in midsummer, with males generally 20 pounds heavier than females. After that, males rapidly outdistance females in weight. By the time females reach 8–9 years they will have attained most of their growth. They will average about 400 pounds in midsummer and rarely exceed 600 pounds. The reason females don't continue to increase in size during their adult years is because they invest so much energy into producing and raising cubs.

Males attain most of their growth by ten years but will continue to add some bulk as they age. A large male will weigh about 1,200 pounds in spring and perhaps 1500–1600 pounds in fall. The largest male taken, based on skull measurements, was shot for a museum specimen in 1952. The skull measured 30 12/16 inches (length plus width), the hide was just over 11 feet wide and nearly 10 feet long, and the body parts, weighed bit by bit, totaled 1,190 pounds minus some body fluids.

It is well known that food abundance, and especially salmon, accounts for the huge size of Kodiak bears. What is less well known is that the diet of bears varies throughout the Kodiak area. Salmon are plentiful on southwest Kodiak Island and bears in that area can feed on salmon from late June through December and, in mild winters, sometimes into January. In this area they often travel from one drainage to another to exploit different salmon runs. On northern Kodiak Island the bears still eat salmon but are more dependent on vegetation and berries, and tend to stay within one or two drainages. Consequently, the annual ranges of females on southwest Kodiak Island average about thirty-five square miles, about three times larger than those in the northern part.

The list of sites where bears congregate to feed is not limited to salmon streams. On a few selected areas of Kodiak and Afognak Islands, bears will spend considerable time on beaches. There they feed on winter-killed deer, marine mammals that wash ashore, and little arthropods, called "beachhoppers," that live in kelp that collects along the shore. In July and early August on central and northern Kodiak Island, many animals can be found in high alpine meadows grazing on sedges, grasses, and forbs. The bears move higher as the snow drifts melt, because they are seeking the newly emerging plants that have the highest protein content. This diet is particularly important to sows with cubs.

One of our most surprising discoveries was that a few bears on Kodiak don't feed on salmon at all. We radio-tracked one female on the Spiridon Peninsula for over ten years and never located her on or near a stream with spawning fish. A couple of other animals were followed for more than five years without showing interest in salmon. What all of this means is that Kodiak is an especially rich and diverse landscape and that

Food abundance and especially salmon accounts for the huge size of Kodiak bears (Howie Garber/wanderlustimages.com).

bears are able to adapt and prosper in virtually all of Kodiak's lush habitat. The important thing, again, is to keep that habitat intact and in the natural state preferred by bears.

Even the denning habits of Kodiak bears vary between areas. On northern Kodiak most animals are in their dens by mid-November, 2–3 weeks earlier than bears on southwest Kodiak. We believe that late-season availability of salmon accounts for delayed denning on southerly areas. Kodiak Island is more mountainous in the north and bears from that region tend to den on steeper slopes and at higher elevations. We found the most unusual denning habits on the Aliulik Peninsula of southern Kodiak. There, bears dug dens in low benchland at less than 500 feet above sea level. Often, bears didn't enter dens until late December or January and it was common for animals to dig two or more dens during one season. Occasionally a bear would not den at all and one large boar never denned the four consecutive years we radio-tracked him.

We found that Kodiak bears were consistent in the order that various sex and age groups entered and left dens. Females generally entered dens earlier than males and pregnant females usually were the first. In spring, the order was reversed. Males were first to emerge, sometimes as early as March. Single females and females with old cubs usually emerged during late April to early May and females with new cubs were the last, often coming out in late May but sometimes not until late June or rarely, early July.

Although one would think that the abundant resources of Kodiak would result in high productivity among its bears, that doesn't seem to be the case. For Kodiak bears, the important parameters that dictate production are similar to those of brown bears along the coastal mainland of Alaska as well as the interior grizzly populations. On average, females produce their first cub litter at 6 or 7 years of age and don't wean their first litter until about 9.5 years. And, the average interval between weaned litters is almost 4 years. Over a 16-year span we observed the fate of over 150 litters and found that although most litters contained 2 or 3 cubs (2.4 average), only 45 percent of those cubs survived to be weaned and joined the population as subadults. Some cubs are killed by other bears, some drown in rivers. Others simply become weak and die for a variety of reasons, such as malnutrition and separation from their mother.

One of the most intriguing questions about females and offspring is, "why are cubs weaned at different ages?" The families usually separate in May and June, but about half of the time females retain litters into the third year, when cubs are nearly 2 1/2 years old, and the remaining litters are weaned in the fourth year. On two occasions we even had marked females that kept their young until the fifth year. It doesn't seem to be a characteristic of individual animals, because we know of some females that were inconsistent in how long they kept different litters intact. Females come into estrus and are courted by males soon after they wean cubs, but the specific behavior patterns that lead to weaning are largely unknown. If the presence of a male nearby can initiate the process, then perhaps age of weaning may depend somewhat on chance. There could be other factors as well.

One thing we know for certain is that Kodiak bears have a low reproductive rate. And that is why bear managers direct so much attention at minimizing mortality of adult females. It takes several years for a female to reach her productive years and even then she probably will raise no more than five litters and five or six individual cubs to adulthood. Because of this low rate, it is extremely important to keep essential habitats intact and to closely monitor population trends. If a decline in habitat quality and/or bear density goes undetected, it may take years and years, if ever, to bring about a successful recovery.

BEAR POPULATION DENSITY & DESTINY

Bear density, either actual or relative, is one of the key information needs of a bear manager. It is also one of the most difficult to obtain. For a period of over ten years, one of our main goals was to develop reliable census methods and estimate bear numbers in various areas of Kodiak. Using radio-collared bears and aerial survey techniques we determined bear densities in three widely separate and contrasting habitats. The estimates ranged from 75 to 90 bears per 100 square miles. The key to this procedure was learning how well we could sight bears from survey aircraft in different types of cover. We found that in brushy, canyon country we only saw about 30 percent of the animals, while in more open

The future of Kodiak bears is bright but certainly not assured (Scott Stouder).

terrain we spotted almost 55 percent of the animals. We then used this information and the same aerial survey techniques to expand our work to additional areas on Kodiak. Overall, we surveyed about 20 percent of Kodiak Island and used that information to estimate numbers for the entire island. The end result was an estimate of 2,600 bears for Kodiak Island and 3,000 for the entire archipelago. Our data showed that at any one time about 53 percent of the population will be composed of solitary animals, 17 percent will be adult females with offspring, and those offspring will make up about 30 percent of the population.

Because Kodiak is a landscape of remarkable diversity, it is no surprise that bear density varies from one area to the next. Some of the rocky, glacier country as well as small offshore islands have very low densities, in the range of 10–20 animals per 100 square miles. At the other end of the scale is the Karluk Lake drainage, an area of about 120 square miles that is without parallel in terms of beauty, diversity, and bear habitat. In spring and late fall the area supports a population of about 180 animals. In summer additional bears move in to exploit Karluk's rich salmon resources and the population swells to more than 200. This congregation of bears is unmatched worldwide.

Because the Karluk Lake area is such a special place and supports so many bears, it is also a magnet for people. As more people become aware of Karluk Lake and other unique places on Kodiak, the problem of balancing public use with protection of bear habitat becomes more difficult. For this reason, we have conducted several studies at Karluk Lake to gain more information on how human activities affect bears.

Some of the most rewarding work at Karluk was time spent at observation camps located high on the slopes. From there we could track both people and bears without affecting their activities. Additionally, it was a rare opportunity to observe movement, fishing, and behavior patterns of bears. We focused our attention on the O'Malley and Thumb Lake basins, as those were the areas that attracted the most bears.

At O'Malley we learned that some bears quickly became accustomed to humans as long as the activities of people were predictable. As a consequence, people that participated in a highly regulated bear viewing program were rewarded with close-up photos and observations of bears. On the other hand, mixed patterns of public use, for example bear viewing, hiking, and fishing at different times and sites, disturbed the animals and reduced bear use of the O'Malley area.

Observations at Thumb River added to our knowledge. There we studied a highly controlled bear viewing program conducted on Native-conveyed land. It was especially interesting to watch subadults who had been offspring of highly habituated (accustomed or tolerant of people close by) females in previous years. These subadults were low on the bear pecking order and usually avoided or were chased by the adults. Females with cubs were particularly rough on them. So they sought comfort and companionship with others of the same status. These subadults would often travel and fish together, and spent countless hours engaged in wrestling matches. These animals had become habituated to people as cubs and retained that tolerance as subadults. It's likely that the female subadults will eventually bring their cubs to the Thumb area and add to the enjoyment of future bear viewers.

People who participated in the highly controlled bear viewing programs at O 'Malley and Thumb were able to observe and enjoy many habituated animals. What they didn't see were the bears that rarely or never came to sites used by people. This was especially true of adult males but included all sex and age classes. The lesson we learned is that bears are very individualistic in their interactions with humans. Just because some animals adapt to people doesn't mean that others aren't being forced away from important habitats.

Another problem with bears and humans involves bears becoming too tolerant or even aggressive towards people. Bears are extremely intelligent and quickly learn that some people, through carelessness or a lack of knowledge, represent a source of food. Failure to properly dispose of garbage or inadequate precautions with game meat at hunting camps are examples. Unfortunately, this often results in the needless killing of bears. Some loss of animals to defense of life or property kills (known as DLPs) is unavoidable, but a large reduction in this loss would occur if people would take the time to learn more about bear behavior and the proper measures to avoid conflicts.

The lessons we learn about bears and people will play a large role in the future management of bears on Kodiak. In some areas it will be necessary to limit or even prohibit public use during periods when bears are especially vulnerable to disturbance. Conversely, there will be other areas where public use can be encouraged. The more people understand and appreciate Kodiak's beauty, diversity, and especially its value as a classic example of ecosystem vitality, the easier it will be to accomplish conservation goals. The welfare of Kodiak bears will be dependent on careful stewardship of all of Kodiak's resources. The key will be continued education of not only the public, but also biologists, managers, administrators, and elected officials who play a role in the management of Kodiak's bears.

The future of Kodiak bears is bright but certainly not assured. As the world's human population continues to grow, we will see more demands on our natural resources. In the Kodiak Archipelago, expanding recreational use, timber harvest, and cabin construction in bear habitat all pose challenges to bear managers. Indirect threats, such as man-caused or climatic changes that affect salmon runs, might have serious compounding effects. Successful management strategies will necessarily include unpopular decisions and compromise. An important concept to keep in mind is that we shouldn't be satisfied in the knowledge that Kodiak bears are merely present. It is the magnitude and dimension of their presence that makes them stand out. The goal should be to use the current situation as a benchmark so that future generations can enjoy Kodiak bears as we do today. We need to know that bears can be found on top of the highest ridges as well as along ocean beaches, that congregations of more than 100 animals still occur along only a mile or two of some streams, and that the landscape is still traversed by giant animals.

"With the descent of salmon fry from two satellite lakes, Thumb and O'Malley, and ten additional spawning streams, Karluk Lake hosts hundreds of millions of young salmon for one to two years prior to their dispersal to the sea."

—DAVE CLINE

Dave Cline is a wildlife conservationist and 30 year Alaska resident. He is chairman of the Kodiak Brown Bear Trust, a Pew Fellow in Marine Conservation, and a consultant to the Alaska Audubon Society and World Wildlife Fund. A northern Minnesota native, Dave worked his way through school with jobs in the iron ore mines and logging camps.

After receiving an advanced degree in fish and wildlife management from the University of Minnesota in 1964, he participated in three National Science Foundation expeditions to the Antarctic, worked 11 years as a wildlife biologist with the U.S. Fish and Wildlife Service, and served 18 years as regional vice president for the National Audubon Society in Alaska.

Dave's 30 years of professional conservation work in Alaska has centered on the design of citizen strategies to protect some of the nation's last great wildlife and wildland spectacles. This has included helping secure establishment of more than 100 million acres of national parks, wildlife refuges, and wilderness areas in Alaska, including the 48,000 acre Alaska Chilkat Bald Eagle Preserve.

Karluk Lake (Dave Cline).

CHAPTER 4

RIVERS OF SALMON, VALLEYS OF BEARS

DAVE CLINE

What if you were to learn that some 56,000 acres of prime Alaska wilderness could be protected for less than the cost of a strip mall? And that on these lands lived an astounding congregation of wild creatures—Kodiak brown bears, hundreds of bald eagles, more wild salmon than in all of the forty-eight contiguous states—along with two wild rivers featuring some of the finest fishing in the world. Which would you choose: to have these lands managed as part of the Kodiak NWR, or left unprotected for eventual sale and development?

This is the choice to be made concerning the Karluk and Sturgeon river drainages on the southwest side of Kodiak Island. It is here that Alaskan Native landowners are willing to negotiate a conservation easement that would restore the integrity of the Kodiak NWR.

Congressional enactment of the Alaska Native Claims Settlement Act (ANCSA) in 1971 created today's conservation crisis by permitting Kodiak Native corporations to select 310,000 acres from within the refuge. Their selections included lands along the Karluk and Sturgeon rivers and those bordering the north half of Karluk Lake (see map, page 93).

A longstanding goal of the Kodiak Brown Bear Trust and its conservation allies has been to help restore Kodiak NWR to its former greatness through acquisition of Native lands on a "willing seller" basis or through conservation easement—in other words, to do what is best for the refuge and its wildlife in a manner that is fair to the people who have lived here a very long time.

Some 56,000 acres of Karluk and Sturgeon lands have been packaged together by Department of Interior (DOI) officials in their negotiations with the landowner, Koniag Incorporated, the regional Native corporation representing all Native shareholders in the Kodiak Archipelago.

Although these good-faith negotiations hold promise, the Kodiak Brown Bear Trust continues to urge both DOI and Koniag to meet at the bargaining table until all differences are resolved and a deal is struck. There is simply too much at stake. Fortunately, a seven-year non-development easement was negotiated in 1995 between the U.S. Fish and Wildlife Service and Koniag, wherein the corporation was paid $2 million not to develop its Karluk-Sturgeon lands. So there is still time—until December 2001—to reach agreement.

Other Koniag lands on the lower Karluk River include the 30,000-acre Karluk Reservation. An additional 1,800 acres of Karluk Tribal Council lands border a four-mile stretch of the Karluk River and Karluk Lagoon (see map, page 93). When the former USFWS director Molly Beattie toured Karluk River a few years ago, she was impressed with the beauty and wildness of the reservation lands, and recognized their

Former USFWS director Mollie Beattie at O'Malley Creek (USFWS).

Karluk and Sturgeon River Lands

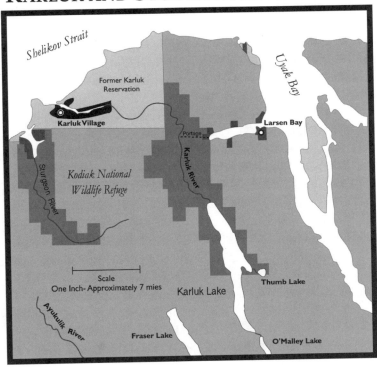

Map of the Karluk and Sturgeon ANCSA inholdings (Eric Cline).

importance to the ecological integrity of the entire river system. Beattie requested these lands be placed in the restoration plan for Kodiak NWR.

Unfortunately, this was never done. But the Kodiak Brown Bear Trust followed up on Ms. Beattie's wishes by contacting Native landowners to see if they were willing to sell a permanent conservation easement. The Trust received a positive response: the Karluk Tribal Council indicated they were willing to discuss all reasonable options for selling a conservation easement on their Karluk River holdings.

The Karluk and Sturgeon river watersheds remain the number one conservation priority of the Trust and its conservation partners. These lands represent the last 20 percent of large inholdings within the boundaries of the original Kodiak NWR. Both river systems are rich in fish and wildlife, with the Karluk drainage justifiably recognized as the biological heart of the refuge.

The extraordinary productivity of the Karluk system is reflected in its high ranking score by the EVOS Trustee Council for potential benefits to six out of eight wildlife species and public uses injured by the *Exxon Valdez* oil spill. These include bald eagle, harlequin duck, river otter, recreation/tourism, cultural resources, and subsistence.

The adjacent and more remote Sturgeon River flows sixteen miles in a northwestern route out of Kodiak NWR into Shelikof Strait. Though data is limited, biologists know the Sturgeon historically supported a large run of chum (dog) salmon (in excess of 91,000 fish), along with pinks (humpbacks), silvers (cohos) and a genetically-unique population of steelhead. The chum salmon run is one of the earliest and most important food sources for brown bears on the refuge. Because access is difficult, the Sturgeon country receives much less public use than the highly popular Karluk. Even so, the sixty-six-square-mile Sturgeon watershed features outstanding opportunities for wilderness recreation.

Both the Karluk and Sturgeon lands are threatened by economic development pressure. The income to be realized through subdividing and selling off lake- and river-front lots is a powerful incentive. Fortunately, roughly $250 million of the $1 billion in civil and criminal oil spill penalties collected from Exxon have been used by the EVOS Trustee Council to buy back most of the prime coastal habitat in the Kodiak Archipelago that was threatened by development. Secretary of the Interior Bruce Babbitt has concluded that "the settlement funds created the largest and most successful environmental restoration project ever attempted." Still, much remains to be done, and both time and money are fast running out.

WILDERNESS PRIMEVAL

My first view of the Karluk River was in the summer of 1972, when I toured Kodiak NWR with former refuge manager Dick Hensel. Dick and I were colleagues on a USFWS wilderness study team. As the person most knowledgeable about the refuge, its bears, and wilderness values, Dick had been assigned the task of preparing a study to determine whether the refuge qualified for inclusion in the National Wilderness Preservation System.

Both Hensel's 1972 Wilderness Study Report and the Kodiak NWR Comprehensive Conservation Plan by the USFWS in 1987 found that refuge lands in the Karluk-Sturgeon drainages meet criteria of the Wilderness Act for size, ownership, natural integrity, apparent natural-ness, solitude, and primitive recreation opportunities. The lands were also found to possess outstanding special values, including some of the finest brown bear habitat in the world; hundreds of bald eagles; a refugium with unique geologic and floral characteristics; the most productive waterfowl habitat in the Kodiak Archipelago; and spawning habitat for steelhead trout, Dolly Varden, Arctic char, and millions of Pacific salmon (U.S. Fish and Wildlife Service 1972 and 1987). A succession of federal ad-ministrations failed to act on those recommendations, and today the lands remain in "de facto" wilderness status.

Although Native inholdings possess similar wilderness values, they are private and so cannot be recommended for wilderness designation. If pur-chased or protected with conservation easements and returned to the refuge, however, they would make valuable additions to the wilderness package.

FIRST PEOPLE

As we circled the meandering Karluk River below the outlet of Kar-luk Lake, Dick pointed out a system of stone weirs in the shimmer-ing waters. He explained that early Native people used stone or log weirs to trap salmon as the fish traveled upstream to spawning grounds. Once congregated in the shallow waters below the weirs, the salmon could be easily killed by means of harpoons designed to penetrate the fish's body. A toggle attached to the harpoon prevented the fish from breaking free. Once the salmon were secured on the riverbank, Native women employed a long, semi-lunar slate blade knife called an "ulu" to butcher the fish. The salmon were eaten raw, cooked, pickled, or dried for winter use.

Who were these early Karluk River salmon fishers? Archaeologists tell us they were a culturally complex Eskimo society called the Alutiiq, who have lived in the Kodiak Archipelago for at least 7,500 years. Amy Steffian of the Alutiiq Museum in Kodiak informed me that at the time of Russian colonization, the Alutiiq lived in large, permanently occupied coastal villages and seasonal fish camps, and maintained an economy based largely on harvesting resources of the sea, especially wild salmon and sea mammals.

"There are forty-six ancient village sites along the twenty-one-mile-long river, with the greatest density in Karluk Lagoon," Steffian said. "This intense occupation reflects the use of the river's predictable salmon resources and a high prehistoric population density. Archaeologists estimate that more than 15,000 Alutiiq people occupied the Kodiak Archipelago prior to Russian colonization."

Owing to its remarkable nearby fish resources, Karluk village was one of the first to be occupied by Russian traders upon their arrival in Alaska. A Russian expedition wintered here in 1785–1786 and built a trading post that was later fortified. The Russians soon adopted the Native's stone-and-log dam technique for catching salmon. By 1827, the Russian American Company was drying some 300,000 Karluk red salmon. They also salted salmon for sale and shipment to their other outposts in what was then known as Russian America (Roppel 1986).

Clark (1984) estimates that the spread of Western diseases caused a massive decline in the Alutiiq population of Kodiak from at least 9,000 at contact to less than 3,000 by the mid-nineteenth century. Today approximately 3,400 people of Alutiiq descent are shareholders in the regional for-profit corporation, Koniag Inc.. The majority, however, have moved from their home villages to the city of Kodiak and beyond. About half the current Alutiiq population now live outside Alaska in the Pacific Northwest. As rightful owners of the Karluk-Sturgeon lands, these shareholders, more than anyone else, will determine the future of these lands.

KARLUK LAKE

I returned to the Karluk-Sturgeon country in 1998 with my ten-year-old stepson, Sasha Romanenko, to join conservation colleagues on a raft trip down the Karluk River. Our aim was to see firsthand the lands at the center of the debate, and to reflect on how we might help resolve the impasse in negotiations.

After a seventy-mile flight southwest from the city of Kodiak, our Grumman Goose aircraft penetrated rain squalls to break out over the river's source, beautiful Karluk Lake (see photograph, page 90). This clearwater lake occupies a long, ice-gouged glacial trench surrounded by lushly vegetated mountains. Karluk is large and deep, covering 9,728 acres with an average depth of 146 feet. In one of its three basins, the lake reaches a maximum depth of approximately 380 feet.

With annual precipitation averaging sixty-eight inches across its 240-square-mile watershed, the Karluk River system is assured an adequate supply of clear, fresh water. Although classified as an oligotrophic lake (meaning low in basic productivity), the infusion of tons of marine nitrogen and phosphorus from millions of salmon carcasses provides a nutrient boost to the lake's phytoplankton. This increased level of primary production (algal biomass) is in turn grazed on by zooplankton—two species of cladocerans and three of copepods. The abundance of cladocerans provide salmon fry with ample nutrition to successfully overwinter. This extended residence in fresh water results in highly efficient conversion of zooplankton biomass to smolt biomass and is probably the reason why Karluk Lake annually produces more fish than most temperate lakes in North America (Rounsefell 1958).

With the descent of salmon fry from two satellite lakes, Thumb and O'Malley, and ten additional spawning streams, Karluk Lake hosts hundreds of millions of young salmon for one to two years prior to their dispersal to the sea.

As we circled overhead, I found it comforting to see a beautiful, unpolluted wilderness lake without any sign of development on its shores—no houses, no roads, no lodges, and no industrial plants. Instead, this was home to some of the highest salmon, eagle, and brown bear populations in the world. But all this could change, I knew, unless we succeeded in returning the lakeshore to protected status.

BEAR COUNTRY

Much of the mainstem Karluk River is too wide and deep for large numbers of bears to fish successfully. The river's upper reaches and the lands surrounding Karluk Lake, however, are perfect brown bear country. Ninety percent of Karluk-Sturgeon's 200 to 300 bears are found here. All of the habitat components essential to brown bears are present: well-drained den sites in the high country; ideal feeding grounds that provide choice plants, roots, berries, and salmon; excellent escape cover; and wilderness isolation with minimal human activity. This is particularly critical habitat for females with cubs, the most important component for sustaining the species.

Lateral streams to Karluk Lake are also ideal for mature male bears, offering abundant salmon in close proximity to cover. Late-spawning red salmon along the lakeshore provide an added food source for bears late in the year, particularly females with cubs and subadults. Some lake tributaries and the mainstem Karluk and Sturgeon rivers attract even later spawning silver salmon, a bonanza for the bears. Fall-spawning cohos along the upper reaches of Silver Salmon Creek are ideally suited for wary mature male bears. The outwash of dead salmon in October and November from spawning streams is an important source of protein for bears just prior to hibernation.

The availability of salmon from June to November, and sometimes into January, provides Karluk-Sturgeon bears with a highly nutritious food source. It is believed this is the main reason Kodiak brown bears have evolved into the largest land carnivores on earth.

Adult male Kodiaks can stand ten feet tall (Dave Menke, USFWS).

"I could understand why the Karluk is considered a flyfisher's delight" (Brad Meiklejohn).

KARLUK RIVER

After a brief stop at the USFWS field headquarters on Camp Island in Karluk Lake, we headed north to the outlet during my 1998 field trip and disembarked on the beach. Here we found the Karluk River in flood stage. Difficult fishing, ideal rafting.

As the trip began, I was immediately impressed by the abundance of waterfowl: diving ducks, including common and red-breasted mergansers, goldeneyes and harlequin ducks, were especially prevalent. Ducks of the dabbling variety—mallard, pintail, green-winged teal, and widgeon—sprang into flight from expansive wetlands bounding the river.

The twenty-one-mile-long Karluk is one of the world's most prolific salmon rivers. The runs include all five species of Pacific salmon and steelhead, rainbow trout, Dolly Varden, and Arctic char. All are wild populations. Annual salmon escapements in the 1990s reached three million, three times more than the Columbia River system's 2,500 watersheds and 260,000 miles of streams, and ten times more wild salmon than return to all of Oregon's coastal streams combined.

The Karluk sockeye (red) runs have been a mainstay of the Kodiak commercial salmon industry since before the turn of the century. In the late 1800s the Karluk sockeye cannery accounted for 80 percent of Alaska's annual salmon pack. Exploitive fishing practices, however, decimated the bountiful Karluk sockeye, and by the 1920s the runs were so severely depleted the canneries closed. Since the end of that grim era, sockeye populations have steadily regained their size. Today the annual Karluk run is up to about 800,000, roughly two-thirds of its historic level, and proof of nature's resiliency.

Up to two million pink salmon return each year to spawn in the Karluk system. Joining them are approximately 10,000 chinook, 20–40,000 coho, and 10,000 steelhead. This makes for world-class sport fishing. With the largest steelhead population on Kodiak Island, the Karluk rivals the Situk River as Alaska's premier steelhead fishing stream. Adult steelhead move upriver from late August through the winter months, over-winter, spawn, and migrate to sea as kelts from May through July (Begich 1997). Tony Chatto, fishery biologist with the USFWS at Kodiak, reports that Karluk steelhead have been identified as a genetically unique population.

Teams of cannery workers pull salmon beach seines at Karluk Lagoon (circa 1900) (National Archives).

Karluk's canneries accounted for 80 percent of Alaska's salmon pack in the late 1800s (National Archives).

Soon after the purchase of Alaska from Russia in 1867, fish robber barons discovered the Karluk River. Driven by the unique variety of greed that resulted in destruction of America's forests and the seemingly inexhaustible numbers of passenger pigeons, bison, fur seals, and sea otters, these early entrepreneurs employed every conceivable fish-catching technique, from traps to dams, weirs to seines. The salmon runs were intercepted without any regard for the future.

The immense take of salmon at Karluk in 1887 and 1888 attracted the attention of even more speculators looking for extravagant profit. By 1889, eight canneries were packing over 350,000 cases of red salmon (the equivalent of four million fish) for shipment to markets throughout the world. It was reported that by 1892, half the production of Alaska canned salmon came from what seemed an endless number of sockeye salmon swimming upriver each year (Roppel 1986).

A handful of individuals saw trouble ahead. A U.S. Fish Commission agent stated that "unless a Karluk hatchery is established, in addition to protective means, red salmon will be exterminated." (Roppel 1986).

But why stop fishing when a hatchery would in theory replenish runs? This philosophy was expressed in 1887 by Dr. Brown Goode, the second commissioner of Fish and Fisheries, and remained in effect for forty-five years. Two salmon hatcheries were eventually built on the shores of Karluk Lagoon in hope of maintaining a steady supply of fish. But high costs and poor results led to their early closure (Roppel 1982).

It was not until passage of the federal White Act in 1920 and establishment of a fish-counting weir on the lower Karluk River in 1921 that a new era in salmon management began. Sustainable harvests then became the goal of the federal government (Schmidt et al. 1998).

Having traveled many of Alaska's wild rivers, I found the Karluk unique among them in its consistent width, depth, and rate of flow. When not in flood stage I could understand why, "It is a fly fisher's delight, wide and open, fairly shallow in many places, and usually very clear" (Heiner 1998). "Karluk's variety and quality of fishing definitely qualifies it as a top ten river" reported Evan and Margaret Swenson (1992) in their book, *Fishing Alaska.*

Once the Karluk begins to penetrate the coastal foothills, the valley narrows and the current quickens. Here we began to see bald eagles in abundance and the occasional brown bear foraging on distant slopes. In other parts of the world the foragers would likely be sheep, goats, or cattle, not bears.

Looking up from the river, the traveler sees a mostly treeless, rolling landscape best characterized as coastal tundra-heath. Only on the warmer, better-drained sites along streams and sidehills do occasional stands of black cottonwoods appear. It's here that bald eagles prefer to build their bulky nests.

The Karluk-Sturgeon lands have cold-temperature soils formed in volcanic ash overlying gravelly glacial till or bedrock. They consist mostly of undecomposed, unfrozen organic matter. Combined with ample rainfall and moderate temperatures, the soils support a lush vegetative cover even in this subarctic life zone. No economically valuable mineral deposits or oil and gas reserves are known to occur (U.S. Fish and Wildlife Service 1987).

River-bottom wetlands are characterized by a plant community typical of arctic Alaska, with dwarf birch, lowbush cranberry, Labrador tea, cloudberry, sedges, lichens, and mosses predominating. Colorful marsh marigolds bloomed along ponds and river margins as we passed.

To the adventurous, the temptation to hike from the river to the high country may prove irresistible. But a word to the wise: be prepared for tough going. Not only is the thick vegetation in subalpine meadows shoulder-high, but the interspersed shrub thickets of Sitka alder, willow, resin birch, and elderberry are almost inpenetrable. And the going is steeply uphill. Most serious hikers wait until after a heavy fall frost to traverse such jungle-like terrain.

Still, the scenery is exceptional. Fireweed, cow parsnip, geranium, goldenrod, wild celery, and false hellbore are interspersed in thick stands of bluejoint grass. Chocolate lily, yarrow, monkshood, starflower, and Jacob's ladder add splashes of color to the meadows.

Once the heights are reached, views can be spectacular. Along ridgelines and moderate alpine slopes the hiker passes over a living mat of Aleutian heather, crowberry, bearberry, cranberry, willow, moss, and lichens. Only on steeper, wind-swept promontories do rock outcrops and barrens appear.

The only structures along the entire Karluk River are five cabins. All are now owned by Koniag Incorporated (one at the lake outlet and four at what's known as the Portage) and available for use through advanced reservation. Rates vary from $100–$200 per day for two to six people. We stayed in one our first night and found it snug, clean, and well-maintained.

Koniag has long been willing to discuss a conservation easement that would return management of its Karluk-Sturgeon land to the Kodiak NWR. In doing so, the corporation would turn a currently unprofitable asset into a dividend stream to help secure an economic future for its shareholders. Simultaneously, the villager's subsistence use would be afforded permanent protection. Offering local people the first opportunity for possible future concessionaire operations on refuge lands would be another incentive to reach a deal.

At this time Koniag is experiencing considerable difficulty preserving the status quo and preventing further degradation of its lands. "Too much pressure in too small an area" is the way Chief Executive Officer Uwe Gross describes it. He says Koniag simply doesn't have the resources to enforce its public-use policies. Income from license and permit sales does not cover expenses. At present, says Gross, Koniag loses more than $50,000 a year "to deal with public access problems."

Koniag's veteran manager of lands and resources, John Merrick, says the biggest problems are associated with increased sport fishing pressure along the Karluk River. "While the corporation desires to maintain high-quality sport fishing and to minimize confrontations with bears, too many visitors are not cooperating." Trash, garbage, and fish waste left behind by irresponsible anglers litter the landscape and constitute serious attractants to bears. Merrick likens favored fishing holes along the river to "hog wallows."

"Meat fishing," whereby individual anglers catch and ship out daily limits of fish over an extended period of time, is another problem. Although Koniag condemns such practices, it is getting no help from the state to prohibit them, according to Merrick.

There is also the problem of habitat degradation along a 2.5-mile trail connecting the village of Larsen Bay to what is known as the Portage Site, located just below a section of the river used for float plane landings. Off-road vehicles driven along this narrow public easement have scarred the land as drivers fan out, sometimes more than a quarter-mile, to avoid ruts in muskeg areas.

Below the Portage cabins, the river valley narrows and the current quickens, as the Karluk penetrates the 1,000 to 2,000 foot-high coastal mountains. We soon entered the 35,000-acre Karluk Reservation. This was established by the U.S. Department of the Interior on May 22, 1943, to fulfill its moral and legal obligations to protect the "economic rights" of the Karluk Village Natives (Case 1984). The reservation system was not expanded to the other villages in the refuge, which had to wait until 1971 to receive their land entitlement. Reservation lands are wild and un-developed and the most rugged and scenic along the river's entire course. Some of the best fishing spots are found along this stretch. Protection of reservation lands will be essential to maintaining the ecological in-tegrity of the Karluk River ecosystem.

At the end of our two-day float trip on the Karluk River, we were guests of Arthur and Freida Panamaroff at their Karluk Spit Lodge. With the snow-capped peaks of the Alaska Range glittering in the sun across the forty mile-wide Shelikof Strait, we watched an occasional seal and sea lion pursue salmon through the surf and into the mouth of the Karluk. As we sipped hot coffee, Arthur, who was born next door fifty-eight years ago, reminded us that his early Alutiiq ancestors lived in nearby sod houses called ciqiluaqs (barabaras in Russian) for at least 800 years.

With the arrival of Europeans and their exploitive practices in the eighteenth century, the Alutiiq's world and that of the Karluk's salmon were turned upside down. Yet despite its sometimes tragic history, abun-dant salmon again inhabit this still-wild river. Watching my Russian-American stepson and two local Alutiiq boys fishing together upstream, I concluded that we simply must do what is necessary to ensure it will al-ways be this way.

CONSERVATION CONCERNS

Despite the efforts of Native landowners working with the USFWS to protect their Karluk-Sturgeon lands, this region, along with its salmon and bears, is in jeopardy. Increasing pressure from visitors and the persistent economic incentive for Natives to develop their lands are ongoing threats to conservation.

Chinook run fish camp in the Karluk Reservation (Douglas H. Grann).

If Native landowners are left with no choice but to develop or subdivide and sell, the story of the Karluk might parallel that of the Kenai River. Rampant development and intensifying public use are now a serious threat to the Kenai's world-class salmon runs, the disruption of which would threaten the Kenai Peninsula's brown bear population.

Rural subdivisions for backcountry cabins and lodges on Karluk-Sturgeon lands would be accompanied by further demands—for construction of airstrips for year-round access, even roads in the future. This would result in the loss of wilderness, fragmentation and loss of wildlife habitat, and an increase in human-bear encounters, with bears the inevitable losers.

The state of Alaska continues to encourage unobstructed access to Karluk-Sturgeon lands and waters consistent with its policy of maximum sustained yield of fish and game. Unfortunately, the quality of the visitor's experience, along with sportsmanship and wilderness values, are sometimes compromised in the process. This leads to trespassing problems on private lands, overcrowding and streambank erosion at popular fishing holes, and damage to soil and vegetation along public easements such as the Portage ORV trail. In contrast, a policy addressing wilderness values would encourage only dispersed low-density, low-impact visitation.

Meanwhile, Native landowners and state and federal management agencies are under pressure to allow airboats, jetboats, and other powerboats on the Karluk and Sturgeon rivers, along with all-terrain vehicles on the uplands. All cause disturbance to wildlife and damage to habitat and wilderness values, and should not be allowed.

The greatest potential for conflict with bears and wilderness values is livestock grazing. Although Native-owned lands do possess some grazing potential for cattle and buffalo, livestock operations elsewhere on Kodiak Island have inevitably led to demands for bear control. Such enterprises are simply incompatible with Kodiak brown bear conservation.

The Bureau of Reclamation has identified the outlet of Karluk Lake into the Karluk River as having hydroelectric potential. As unlikely as construction of a future dam here may seem, such an obstacle would have devastating effects on the river's prolific salmon runs.

Non-indigenous animals pose another threat. Should previously introduced Sitka black-tailed deer and reindeer become overpopulated, they could compete with brown bears by over-browsing favored berry bushes. If too many beaver, another introduced species, are permitted to dam spawning streams, the availability of salmon to bears and eagles could be reduced.

What does all of this mean for the future of Kodiak brown bears, salmon, bald eagles, and their wilderness haunts? The conclusion, to me, seems obvious: protect these irreplaceable lands while the opportunity exists, or watch them slowly unravel and lose their wild character like so much of the American landscape.

By purchasing conservation easements on the Native-owned Karluk-Sturgeon lands, we can preserve the Kodiak wilderness ecosystem, a wild and intact place linking land and sea, a place of salmon, brown bears, and bald eagles. In doing so, we can also help sustain local economies, and provide wilderness experiences to last a lifetime for those who cherish wildlife and wild places.

REFERENCES

Bean, Tarleton H. 1890. *Report on the salmon and salmon fishing rivers of Alaska,* Washington D.C.: U.S. Government Printing Office.

Begich, Robert N. 1997. *Assessment of the 1995 return of steelhead to the Karluk River, Alaska.* Alaska Department of Fish & Game, Fishery Data Series no. 97–6.

Case, David S. 1984. *Alaska natives and the law.* Fairbanks: University of Alaska Press, , Alaska.

Clark, Donald W. 1992. *Archaeology of Kodiak: the quest for origins and its implications for North Pacific prehistory.* Anthropological Paper of the University of Alaska, Fairbanks 24 (1 & 2): 109–126.

Finney, B.P. 1998. *Long-term variability in Alaskan sockeye salmon abundance determined by analysis of sediment cores.* North Pacific Anadromous Fish Commission Bulletin 1:388–95.

Heiner, Dan. 1998. *Fishing Alaska's wild rivers.* Mechanicsburg, Pennsylvania: Stackpole Books.

Roppel, Patrcia. 1982. *Alaska's salmon hatcheries 1891–1959.* Alaska Historical Commission Studies in History No. 20, Anchorage, Alaska.

Roppel, Patricia. 1986. *Salmon from Kodiak: an history of the salmon fishery of Kodiak Island, Alaska.* Alaska Historical Commission Studies in History No. 216, Anchorage, Alaska.

Rounsefell, G.A. 1958. Factors causing decline in sockeye salmon of Karluk River, Alaska. *Fisheries Bulletin* 58: 83–169.

Safina, Carl. 1997. *Song for the blue ocean: encounters along the world's coasts and beneath the seas.* New York: Henry Holt and Company.

Schmidt, Dana, Stan R. Carlson, Gary B. Kyle, and Bruce P. Finney. 1998. Influence of carcasses-derived nutrients on sockeye salmon production of Karluk Lake, Alaska: importance in the assessment of an escapement goal. *North American Journal of Fisheries Management* vol.18 no. 4: 743–63.

Schwarz, Len. 1997. *Area management report for the recreational fisheries of the Kodiak and Alaska Peninsula/Aleutian Islands regulatory areas, 1996.* Fishery Management Report No.92–2, Alaska Department of Fish & Game, Anchorage, Alaska.

Steffian, Amy F. and Richard A. Knecht. 1998. Karluk one. Weston, Connecticut: Pictures of Record, Inc.

Steffian, Amy F. 1996. *Archeological salvage at Karluk one: report from the 1995 field season.* Alutiiq Museum and Archeological Repository, Kodiak, Alaska.

Swensen, Evan and Margaret. 1992. *Fishing Alaska.* Helena, Montana: Falcon Publishing Company, Inc.

U.S. Fish and Wildlife Service. 1987. *Kodiak National Wildlife Refuge comprehensive conservation plan, environmental impact statement, wilderness review.* Anchorage, Alaska.

U.S. Fish and Wildlife Service. 1986. *The controlled addition of inorganic nitrogen and phosphorus into Karluk Lake. Draft Environmental Assessment.* Anchorage, Alaska.

U.S. Fish and Wildlife Service.1972. *Kodiak National Wildlife Refuge: wilderness study report.* Anchorage, Alaska.

Karluk River empties into the Shelikof Strait (Brad Meiklejohn).

*"True wilderness, however, is not renewable, and the chance
to ensure that truly wild places continue to exist is fast becoming
a rare thing."*

—*COLLEEN RANKIN*

*Lifelong Alaskan Colleen Rankin helps operate a remote lodge
in Blue Fox Bay, located on the northwest corner of Afognak Island. Colleen found herself vitally interested in the outcome of the
Afognak land negotiations in the oil spill restoration plan. She became an effective advocate for the largest possible habitat protection
agreement and in this chapter shares her personal experiences and
appreciation for the land, waters, and wildlife of Afognak.*

*Biologists evaluating 1,500 miles of oiled beaches throughout the
oil spill region found that Native-owned lands on northern Afognak
Island held the optimum habitat values for fish and wildlife species
injured by the spill. Since EVOS restoration aimed to protect high
quality breeding, nesting, and rearing habitats for fish and wildlife,
the effort to protect Afognak lands from future human-caused habitat disturbance became a benchmark for the plan's overall success.*

*The fact that Kodiak and Afognak Native corporations were set
to log these very same critical habitat areas on Afognak put Native
economic well-being on a collision course with the habitat protection goals of oil spill restoration. Following lengthy, often contentious
negotiations, the EVOS Trustee Council acquired large tracts of old-
growth coastal rainforest in 1998 for a price of $70.5 million.*

*Afognak supports the westernmost forest in North America
(EVOS Trustee Council, Daniel Zatz).*

CHAPTER 5

AT HOME IN THE AFOGNAK WILDERNESS

COLLEEN RANKIN

Afognak. The name alone implies mystery; the place itself is one of intrigue. The first Russian ships passing down what is today known as Shelikof Strait caught only glimpses of fog-shrouded peaks and the roar of breakers on rocky cliffs, warning of a hazardous coastline.

This is an island of timeless beauty, washed by turbulent north seas, yet in the path of what seems to be inevitable change. It lies just north of Kodiak Island and at 740 square miles is the second largest of the thirteen main islands of the Kodiak Archipelago. For those fortunate enough to have seen it, Afognak is recognized as one of the wildest and most beautiful islands in Alaska. The 300-mile-long coastline is characterized by towering cliffs, sandy beaches, rocky islets, and rich tidal estuaries. Protected bays and glacial carved fjords reach over nine miles inland, a ragged frame of the rugged interior.

Afognak is our home. Thanks to a private owner who has a strong sense of history, attachment to, and desire to keep the land as it is, Jerry Sparrow and I live at, and operate a small lodge at, the site of a former herring saltry in Blue Fox Bay, on Afognak's remote northwest coast. It is the only private parcel surrounded by what is now Kodiak NWR lands.

Along with my home-schooled children, Ryan and Indianna, we live a semi-subsistence lifestyle, and keep our impact to a minimum. The majority of our food comes from our surroundings and makes it easy for us to understand why the Kodiak Archipelago originally supported such an incredibly healthy population of Native people. In season we harvest halibut, salmon, deer, elk, berries, mushrooms, and kelp. A modest garden provides vegetables in summer.

Our livelihood comes from hosting a select and limited number of guests seeking an escape from their busy lives and civilized worlds, and who share an appreciation of the peace, beauty, and sometimes drama offered in this wild place. We encourage a laid-back, no-frills kind of experience. There are very few places left that come close to being as undisturbed as Afognak, and watching the reaction of people experiencing the pristineness for the first time is very satisfying. Part of our reward is spreading an awareness of the fragility and rarity of these places.

One of the opportunities inclement weather provides is time spent in the company of others with no modern interruptions. At times storms force us indoors where things are more hospitable. The warmth of the kitchen is most welcome after being at the receiving end of one of mother nature's "attitudes." People that normally have nothing in common find themselves bonded together from their shared experience and the powerful feelings they are left with.

Some of our best moments are spent at the kitchen table with guests, wood stove glowing, coffee cups in hand, admiring the steep forested mountains of the Red Peak and Devils Paw ranges across Blue Fox Bay. Rising out of the sea to heights of over 2,400 feet, they have many moods, sometimes beckoning you for a climb, where from the top the mainland of Alaska is visible in detail over seventy miles away. At other times their ridges are wrapped in wisps of mist, creating a vision of awesome yet delicate power. Some days they stand invisible in a curtain of fog and create a hazard to local float plane pilots.

Since we live on a smaller 180-acre island off Afognak, we depend on skiff travel intensely; the ocean and tides dominate our everyday lives more than any other factor. High tides mean towing driftwood home for our stoves, and being able to navigate waters that are normally too shallow. Low tide is a wonderful time to explore the shoreline from our kayaks, but newly exposed reefs can cause a hazard to boat travel. Reading the tide wrong can mean your boat goes dry and you get to wait for it to come in before you can leave.

The wind and the ocean form a partnership that has always greatly affected the lives of people living in the Kodiak Archipelago. From ancient hunters in their bidarkas to modern day commercial fishermen, those of us who depend on the sea for travel carry an alertness to changing weather conditions. This can help avoid a mistake, which may only mean not getting back home and spending an unplanned night on a beach, but could be much more grave.

Staying alive can be a combination of good luck and listening to the forecast. This determines whether boating the six miles over to Port William to meet the weekly mail plane is an option for us, something we look forward to since there is no telephone at our place. We tell ourselves that technology hasn't brought the cost of a satellite unit into a reasonable financial window. But deep inside we are reluctant to break the stillness and bring the outside world into this place of natural rhythms. We recognize and love the unique pace of life here.

Calm, sunny days usually arrive on the tail of a storm and the clean air left behind is charged air with a vibrancy that one of our regular guests refers to as "antiseptic." At these times we can't hold ourselves back, and leaving our local island work behind, head out to re-discover a favorite spot.

Mist, fog, and rain dominate most of the time. Hearing that Eskimos in northern Alaska have over fifty words for snow, we have wondered if the first people of this archipelago didn't have at least as many words for rain. From a mild dampness in the air to a horizontal torrent, it comes in any form imaginable.

Such a wet environment (over sixty inches annually) is not what most people would consider an ideal spot to vacation or live in. It is the rain, though, that enables Afognak to grow its great forest of giant Sitka spruce.

Protected bays and glacial carved fiords reach over nine miles inland (Scott Stouder).

Winter snows reach depths of up to 90 inches, and force the local Sitka black-tailed deer and Roosevelt elk down out of the mountains and onto the beaches to forage on kelp and other sea plants that wash up there. In particularly snowy times, both species experience heavy mortality from starvation. We find carcasses of the weakest in the forest and on the beaches. During a bleak winter this is good fortune for bald eagles, ravens, crows, magpies, and foxes, who leave just a few scattered bones when they are through.

INTO THE RAINFOREST

Whether one approaches Afognak by plane or boat, the sharp contrast experienced when entering this primeval forest is overwhelming. Starting out on a beach where winter storms with 120 knot winds have left trees of enormous size tossed in a careless tumble, it is obvious that extreme things happen here. Prints of otter, deer, fox, numerous birds, and giant brown bear in the sand tell that life moves forward here with-

"The number of bears on Afognak remains a mystery" (Brad Meiklejohn).

out the interference of man. Each beach has its own story, from the pattern of tracks to the sounds of the ocean resounding against the rocks.

This dynamic world at the shore hardly prepares you for the serenity you encounter when you step off the beach and into the moss-draped world of giant Sitka spruce trees. The most westerly coastal rainforest in North America, there is a mix of fragility and power here. Peeling back a layer of moss on the lower branches reveals a layer of ash left over seventy years ago and makes you wonder what other secrets are hidden in this place. Under the protective canopy is a climate of filtered light and dampness that nurtures a wide array of vegetation. Large ferns, devils club, salmonberries, blue and elderberries grow in healthy numbers, along with many wildflower species that prefer the shade. The decay of fallen trees only adds to the richness of the environment here. These horizontal trunks serve as nurseries for the seedlings in the next cycle of life in this forest.

The mossy forest floor is so plush it absorbs the sound of your footsteps, yet is so fragile you can follow the depressions left by generations of bears where they have walked to feeding grounds and winter dens. To be in the intimate presence of these ancient trails feels like a privilege and reminds us that we are in their world. To some this may feel intimidating, yet to us it is a relief to find a place where nature has been allowed to carry on.

Having lived and observed wildlife in many areas of Alaska and Canada, we believe that many species develop character traits unique to their local habitat. In this world of heavy cover, the animals are more aloof. The shyness and desire for seclusion demonstrated by elk, deer, and especially bears make it a real challenge to view them.

For us, it is the bear that best characterizes the spirit of the wilderness. To be on the beaches, mountains, or in the forests of Afognak is to be aware of his existence. Even when he is not visible, his presence seems as real as the moss hanging on the trees around you. Many times, hiking on a snowy day, we have crossed his freshly made tracks, knowing he was just moments ahead and it was he who avoided us.

When you consider that these islands of Kodiak and Afognak have the largest bears in the world and yet nothing that could be considered prey other than salmon existed before the introduction of deer in the

1920s, it makes you reconsider the ferocious reputations of these giants. For eons they were just fisher bears with over fifty percent of their diet being vegetarian. Yet they grew to enormous size. It seems a paradox that the largest of these legendary creatures didn't get that way by being an aggressive hunter. He is a true example of thriving on the natural richness of this area.

But their lives are not without challenges. We see sows with cubs swimming offshore to small maritime islands to spend most of the summer, where they forage on bird eggs and new plant shoots. We think, though, that part of their reason for braving the sea is to escape the threat big male bears pose to cubs. The number of bears on Afognak remains a mystery, since they are difficult to find and count in the forested terrain.

The delicate and elusive Sitka black-tailed deer spread north to Afognak after being introduced on Kodiak in 1924. They add a delicate dimension to the forest, having the opposite presence of the bear. While we love to see nature left alone, we view the addition of these beautiful creatures as a very positive thing. In our area, we say there are two types of deer, forest deer that stay in the lowlands year round, and mountain deer. They prefer the alpine areas, browsing on the grass, fireweed, and other mountain plants by night, and taking cover in alder thickets by day. You'll find them near the highest peaks where the cool breezes give them relief from biting insects and the open vistas enable them to better spot predators. Only after the onset of winter do they move down into the treeline.

Another transplant to Afognak is the Roosevelt elk. They are much rarer than deer and their alertness makes them a challenge to see on foot. We see them on mountain hikes, where they always seem to be just one peak away. They now range throughout most of the island, having spread from their transplanting spot on the south end near Litnik Bay.

It is believed that the name Litnik may have come from the Russian word "Elitnik" which means, "a place where fish are dried and prepared." With salmon-rich Afognak river and lake at its back door, this seems likely.

Litnik is near the original native community of Afognak village located at the south end of the island. Peter Noya, who grew up there as a boy, tells a wonderful story about his mother sending him and his brother

Archaeological house pit excavation on Afognak's coast (Dig Afognak!).

out to chase the elk away from the clothes line, where they were catching her freshly hung laundry on their antlers.

A busy village at the turn of the century, the number of people had dwindled down to 178, when the 1964 Good Friday earthquake created tidal waves that destroyed their homes and lowered the village site 5–6 feet. The survivors moved 12 miles south to Kizhuyak Bay on Kodiak Island, where they named their new village Port Lions, in honor of the Kodiak Lions club, who had offered financial and other help in the move.

This was the last native village on Afognak, but with more than thirty-seven archaeological and historical sites identified, the island was once a thriving area for Alutiiq people.

We sometimes see freshly exposed middens on the shores of Afognak and wonder what these ancestors would think if they could glimpse the changes taking place on Afognak today.

Despite its isolation from main flyways, some 160 species of birds frequent Afognak's varied habitats. Stellers, jays, magpies, common ravens, crows, bald eagles, and many types of gulls are the most conspicuous as they search open coastlines for favorite foods. Spring and early summer are the best times to enjoy migrant songbirds that include orange-crowed warblers, varied thrush along with Savannah, fox, song and golden-crowned sparrows. Flocks of black-capped chickadees, red-

"It is easy to see why they are known as sea wolves" (EVOS Trustee Council).

Kodiak Bears & the Exxon Valdez

poles, pine siskins, golden-crowned kinglets, and pine grosbeaks prefer the spruce forest. They are kept alert by predators like the northern goshawk, boreal owl, peregrine falcon, and northern harrier. Eighty seabird colonies are located on coastal lands that are at risk and that we would like to see protected. Species most injured by the oil spill and still recovering are marbled murrelets, pigeon guillemots, black oystercatchers, and harlequin ducks. Sheltered bays like Blue Fox attract thousands of wintering waterfowl. These include Barrow and common goldeneyes, greater scaup, buffleheads, harlequin ducks, oldsquaws, black surf and white winged scoters, along with king and Stellar eiders. Other ducks like mallard, green-winged teal, northern pintails, Northern shovelers, and horned grebes favor coastal wetlands.

Because of the abundance of their favorite fish foods, common loons, along with common and red mergansers, also thrive.

The marine mammal life is rich in these waters. No one really knows for sure how many species of whales pass through. When out in our boats in summer we see several types, including minkes and the huge finback, cruising by. Most common, the humpback is spectacular as he bursts out of the ocean breaching as high into the air as he can. We have watched them do this continually for over an hour. Dall porpoise actually seek out our skiff to race us and to ride the wake of our boat; everyone in the skiff has ended up soaking wet but thrilled after these encounters. Pods of Orcas come right into Blue Fox Bay; we see them from our kitchen window year-round as they head for the local seal rocks and explore every corner of the bay. It's easy to see why they are known as Sea Wolves. Though we haven't seen them ourselves, we have heard boats on the local VHF radio reporting sitings of Blue, Beluga, and beaked whales in Shelikof Straits on the west side of Afognak.

The sea otters are the most numerous marine mammal and our favorites. It's especially fun to watch mother otters grab their single pups and dive them to safety. There was one instance where I watched a mother otter continually retrieve her sleeping pup as it was carried down the bay by wind and current while she was below water searching for food. She eventually tired of having to tow him back to her feeding grounds and carried him to a more protected area. We can hear them munching on shellfish, or calling to each other on calm nights. One particular otter often appears just off shore in what appears an attempt to tease our Labrador retriever, Max, into pursuing him. Eventually Max can't resist the temptation and swims out in pursuit. It soon becomes obvious who is the better swimmer.

Some of the most beautiful and peaceful spots on the island are at the mouths of small salmon streams that empty into forest-bordered inlets. On some days we and our guests watch the view from water's edge in company with eagles, gulls, and other shore creatures. Most people are fascinated watching the restless movements in the emerald colored waters, as they respond in unison to shifting tidal and stream currents waiting to move upstream past the waiting bears to spawning grounds. It's a primeval scene and demonstrates how eons of evolution have brought two distinct worlds together—ocean world and island world—in one of the most dramatic displays of nature's bounty. And all without the interference of technological man.

It's at such times that we are reminded of what Carl Safina wrote in *Song for a Blue Ocean:*

"It is not difficult to see why Native people worshipped these fish."

"Imagine an animal that is born in the mountains, travels backward on river currents hundreds of miles to the sea, disappears in the deep oceans for years, and then reappears hundreds of times larger and fights its way into the clouds while fasting, to spawn upon its deathbed."

Beachcombing is a favorite activity and we have yet to come across any human footprints not made by us or our guests in this part of Afognak. Low tide gives us access to an unbelievably productive intertidal world, where we can walk among thick mats of algae to find strange life forms under almost every overturned rock.

It is on these walks along Afognak's shores that the interconnectedness between the land and the sea becomes clear. And this is when we remind ourselves that people must become good stewards of both the land and sea if Afognak's riches are to be sustained. As wildlife biologist Katy Kullitz explains it, "If you want to have marbled murrelets you have to have old growth trees for them to nest in. And if you want salmon, you need to protect streams salmon spawn in. You can't just draw a line at the ocean edge."

Conservation easements can outperform timber income.
(EVOS Trustee Council, Daniel Zatz).

Like other remote places, recent events have made it clear that Afognak, too, is vulnerable to the effects of modern man. No Alaskan will forget the year 1989 when the oil tanker *Exxon Valdez* spilled eleven million gallons of crude into Prince William Sound. At first residents of this archipelago believed our islands were too far away to see any effects. It soon became obvious that the slick was spreading in our direction and oil began appearing on outside beaches. As it turned out, Afognak, neighboring Shuyak Island to the north, and areas of Kodiak Island in the Shelikof Straits were the most heavily oiled of all the areas in the archipelago.

Although most of the oil has been cleaned up by mother nature, there are other threats to this place.

Logging by Native landowners is working its way ever closer to the eastern boundary of the Red Peak unit of the Kodiak NWR.

Needing answers for its shareholders, the timber industry, particularly foreign interests, has provided Native corporation executives with the means to give immediate financial responses. They have been in the timber industry since 1979 and own most of Afognak.

While some believe that deforested land can provide better feeding habitat for wildlife, the negative effects far outweigh the benefits. In the first 3–10 years following a cut, it's true that many traditional browse plants flourish. Then new seedlings grow without any variation in their age. As a result they are very close in size and proximity to each other. Soon the light is blocked out completely from the forest floor and all other plant life is starved out. Eventually some of the young trees themselves die and the cycle of an old forest begins. Estimates are that it takes two hundred years to reach the ancient stage we see on parts of Afognak.

Keeping land in a natural state, however, will provide not only economic benefits but lifestyles for those who wish to share the wilderness with outsiders looking for adventures in a natural setting. In an increasingly overcrowded world, people are coming to value these places. We have guests who have prosperous lives in every other way, but repeatedly return because the solitude and beauty found here is unavailable in most of their world.

Part of what they crave is the simpler way of life we live here, and for those willing to share, through visitor-oriented careers, there is much opportunity.

It would be a shame for changes to take place in one generation that make it impossible for the following ones to be able to choose their own values and lifestyles.

We would like to see more of Afognak remain in a natural state. Through conservation easements and/or land aquisition, it is well worth protecting. We watched part of the process that took place when in 1998, the EVOS Trustee Council and Afognak Joint Venture settled on a price of $70.5 million for 41,750 acres along Afognak's northern coast. It was impressive to witness the cooperation, dedication, and patience on all sides to reach this agreement. But there is still more work to be done, before what is left is irrevocably changed.

Perhaps the question of how many of the remaining oil spill funds should be committed to research projects or land acquisition would be simplified if we view research as the renewable resource that it is. As long as we as humans have an appetite for knowledge, which we seem to have in unquenchable quantities, we can somehow create the funding. True wilderness, however, is not renewable, and the chance to ensure that truly wild places continue to exist is fast becoming a rare thing.

Since we have to find balance in our answers to groups with varied interests, the challenge takes many turns. The simplest question we can think of is: what is priceless or irreplaceable? If we use this as a guideline for making decisions when it comes to doing what we can to preserve those places left that are still true wilderness, it would seem that on Afognak there is a great opportunity we should embrace.

Perhaps the letter we received from a guest wanting to return this year says it best. It began:

"I hadn't planned on coming back to Alaska this year, but the thought of your beautiful island was too much for me."

"Karluk kings are tied to a past older than mastodons and mammoths. The southern end of Kodiak Island, known as the 'Refugium', was spared the scouring effects of the Ice Age glaciers. This lack of genetic interruption is suspected of connecting these fish to a lineage over 80,000 years old."

—SCOTT STOUDER

Award-winning outdoor writer Scott Stouder has wandered the Kodiak Archipelago with a rifle, fishing rod, and camera and provides readers of Kodiak Bears & the Exxon Valdez *with a personal account of back country trips he has taken, offering a glimpse of what future visitors can experience as a result of the EVOS habitat protection agreements.*

Stouder's chapter addresses one of the public's most frequently asked questions more than ten years after the Exxon Valdez *accident, namely, "What is the public's primary benefit out of the $1 billion settlement with Exxon?"*

The biggest part of the answer to that question in the Kodiak Archipelago is, "the protection of 376,000 acres of world class wilderness lands that were all formerly private and closed to access that are now open to the public." When the Kodiak NWR inholding acquisitions and Afognak State Park additions are added to other protected lands in the archipelago, the public can now enjoy an intact world class conservation area larger than Yellowstone National Park.

As American society faces increasing human population and private development sprawl there is a growing desire for open public space. In this context the habitat protection successes from the oil spill settlement seem almost too good to be true.

A chinook and two sockeye salmon returning to spawn (Marion Owen).

CHAPTER 6

IN THE FOOTPRINTS OF THE GREAT BEAR

SCOTT STOUDER

There are still places on this earth where the world works. And as another chrome-bright coho stripped line from my reel and did cartwheels across the ice-blue water of Shelikof Strait I knew Kodiak was one of those places.

When Tim Richardson, executive director of the Kodiak Brown Bear Trust, talked to me about Kodiak two years before, I was skeptical.

"Kodiak has some of the best hunting and salmon fishing in Alaska," he said as we shared coffee near his home in Washington, D.C. He described rivers choked with salmon, protected bays lined with halibut, and mountains with herds of Sitka black-tailed deer. He also described Kodiak as one of the world's most populous homes for brown bears.

I was skeptical. Richardson was a professional political type from the east coast. He might recognize a big bear when he saw one, but how much could he know about good hunting and fishing?

What I had forgotten was that natural systems still work where salmon swell rivers and giant bears dominate the landscape. And where natural systems work, it doesn't matter where you're from or how much you know. Health and abundance are quick teachers.

In 1941, when President Franklin D. Roosevelt established the Kodiak National Wildlife Refuge to "protect the natural breeding and feeding range of brown bears. . .on Kodiak Island," the intent wasn't to preserve a small piece of high altitude rock-and-ice. The 1.9 million-acre refuge of river systems, glacier-carved mountain ranges, and sweeping tundra plains surrounded by a breathtaking marine richness was established to protect the largest land carnivore on the planet. Because of this unique foresight, Kodiak NWR today is a healthy, functioning, ecoregion of wildlife, including salmon and giant bears, bound together by an interlocking web of genetic strings unsurpassed anywhere in the world.

Richardson emphasized that the mountains, rivers, and bays of Kodiak have remained essentially unchanged since humans first set foot here thousands of years ago.

"You don't have to imagine what it looked like when the Alutiiq or the Europeans first saw it," he said. "You can still see it."

For three weeks that first summer I wandered the Kodiak Archipelago with a fishing rod, rifle, and camera. I caught salmon on Afognak and Kodiak islands, hunted deer in the high country, and photographed brown bears along pristine salmon streams. And I fell in love with Alaska's emerald jewel. What I didn't know then was that the arms of Kodiak would encircle me tighter than I could imagine.

On a map Kodiak Island looks like an escapee of Alaska's massive interior. Separated by the Aleutian chain and the Alaska Peninsula from the Bering Sea, the 3,465 square miles of jumbled bays, peninsulas, and mountains are thirty miles across Shelikof Strait from Alaska's mainland. Its 1,000 miles of ragged coastline were scoured out by prehistoric sheets of glacial ice. The island today is constantly hammered and shaped by pounding wind, rain, and waters from 360 degrees of open sea.

The interior is as diverse as its perimeter. Rain-drenched flanks of mountains peppered with spruce and hardwood climb to granite peaks on the east side of the island and slide to bare, tundra plains in the west, where the sprawling rug of grass is cut with ridges, rivers, peninsulas, and bays. The light touches of human influence here, especially on the southern two-thirds of the island, where the bulk of Kodiak NWR lies, are only slight blemishes to its natural beauty. Less than 100 miles of roads scar its velvet skin, and 95 percent of those roads encircle the city of Kodiak.

Seven major river drainages and hundreds of smaller tributaries and streams drain the land. All five of the Pacific salmon species (sockeye, chinook, pink, coho, and chum) return to these icy inland fingers of water; an estimated 70 percent of the salmon caught by Kodiak's commercial fishing industry are born and reared in the rivers and lakes within the Kodiak NWR.

On the warm-blooded side, fourteen different marine mammal

species live in the Kodiak Archipelago, with an estimated 1.5 million seabirds and 150,000 ducks and geese that spend winters on the island. In addition, over 600 bald eagles nest within the refuge making it home to Alaska's largest year-round population of bald eagles.

But fins and feathers aside, the hoof and claw species garner a huge chunk of the public attention on Kodiak. Besides huntable populations of mountain goats hanging onto the granite peaks and approximately 1,200 Roosevelt elk living in the rich mosaic of spruce timber and grass meadows of Afognak Island, Sitka black-tailed deer are the most abundant animals on the archipelago. Approximately 200,000 deer live here, and hunters annually put between 9,000 and 10,000 animals in their freezers.

But by far the most notable and infamous presence are the approximately 3,000 Kodiak brown bear *(Ursus arctos middendorffi)* that live on the islands. Although the average size of an adult is about 800 pounds, some of the giants reach 1,500 pounds and stand over ten feet tall.

Bears are fundamental to the fabric of life on Kodiak. Every living thing on the island, including humans, live in close contact with these extraordinary animals.

A DEER HUNTER'S PARADISE

An August deer hunt was a prime focus during my first visit to Kodiak. What I didn't realize was that the hunting experience would be as much about bears as deer.

Until visiting Kodiak, my personal experience with the bear family had been limited to *americanus*-black bears. And, I've got to admit, never having actually seen one from the *middendorffi* ranks, I was a bit intimidated by the prospect of deer hunting for a week by myself in their front yard.

The sight of a single line of plate-sized tracks ambling up the freshly washed, gravel beach as I unloaded my duffel and rifle from the skiff at Three Saints Bay didn't bolster my resolve. But deer hunting is my life's passion and I wasn't about to let the mere presence of large bears dim the fire.

"You're nuts going up into that high country to hunt deer," Jeff

Aerial photo of a salmon spawning tributary of Long Lagoon (Scott Stouder).

Peterson said with a grin as we stood on the beach near the little inflatable raft we'd used to reach shore. "Wait until late October and November until they come down to you."

Peterson, a native guide from Old Harbor, had brought me to a cabin in Three Saints Bay in his fishing boat.

"Good luck," he said as he clambered into the raft and began rowing back toward the bigger boat anchored offshore. "I'll see you in a week."

I watched the big boat round the point into Sitkalidak Strait before I turned and followed a faint path to a weathered, one-room cabin that would be my home for the next week. It sat next to the mountain in a tall grass meadow circled with wild blueberry and scrub alder. The length of a football field inland from the protected bay, it seemed dwarfed by the towering grass-covered ridges above it.

During the warm summer days deer languish on those high ridges where cool breezes and elevation keep insects and people at bay. For two weeks since I'd been fishing and boating around Kodiak, I'd watched deer through binoculars in that lustrous high country with the lustful eye of a hunter. Sitka black-tailed deer are not indigenous to Kodiak. They were introduced from southeast Alaska in 1924. The deer have flourished and today number in the hundreds of thousands. In the southern part of the island, they're so abundant and the hunting so light that hunting season extends for five months from August through December, with an annual bag limit of four deer per hunter. They aren't hunted heavily until November, when winter snow rut drives them downslope near the beaches.

When I left the cabin and began climbing the next morning, I found out why the high country gets little hunting pressure. There are no trails or easy routes to the ridgetops. Progress from the beach is hand-over-hand through a jungle of salmonberry, elderberry, devils-walking-cane, head-high grass, and scrub-alder thickets. The distance from the curdled vegetation near the beach to the scantily-dressed ridgelines, where normal walking is possible, is less than a mile as a crow flies, but progress is one slow, sweat-drenched foot at a time.

The only reprieve from the morass are tunnels made by brown bears during their summer berry-foraging. A half-ton bear wallowing through thick brush leaves a path wherever it goes. However, following these paths was a mixed blessing. They seldom went in the direction I was headed, and crawling through a brushy tunnel made by a half-ton animal with big teeth, long claws, and a territorial imperative has a built-in fatigue factor.

After swimming through tall grass, devil's club, and salmonberries for nearly two hours, I was nearing the open ground at the top when I staggered backwards into a clearing—of sorts. Wiping the sweat from my eyes I looked around. The scrub-alder was mashed and mowed to the approximate size of a two-car garage, with one Buick-sized piece of earth dished out. My heavy breathing slowed, then stopped as I realized I'd either staggered into the testing grounds for a D–9 bulldozer, or a brown bear bedroom. The sudden sounds of a heavy body breaking brush without a diesel engine convinced me it wasn't a bulldozer, but I blasted up the remaining hillside and stormed into the upper short-grass ridge like I was one.

Once above the brush-belt, standing on shaking legs and picking brush and clothing scraps away from my body, I tried to simultaneously look in all directions. Gasping for breath, I sat down heavily and wondered who was more scared, the bear or me.

"No contest," I thought. "I am."

After sucking lungfuls of air and quelling sudden urges to scream I had a few serious questions about why I had voluntarily invaded the home of giant bears. But after repaying my oxygen debt and patching together my tattered clothing and confidence I calmed considerably and looked around me.

The view stole my refurbished breath.

Under a morning sun the mountain peaks, green ridges, and blue bays stretched to every horizon without a building, road, or blemish. The only sound was silence and the only smell was salt air. Once above the thick, vegetative crown protecting the bays, the ridges radiating down from the granite peaks are carpeted with ankle-high grass that makes walking about as strenuous as strolling through a golf course.

But this golf course was littered with Sitka black-tailed deer. Lots of them. During a week of hunting I would see fifty to sixty deer each day, including dozens of nice bucks. I didn't run into any more bears (although I never climbed that ridge again), but did see tracks where they'd passed in the night.

During the day the mountain solitude, punctuated by the excitement of spotting bucks, made time melt. Every morning at daybreak, after bolting down a bowl of oatmeal, I'd tackle the mountain and spend the long daylight hours watching deer and eagles through binoculars. Every evening I would descend through the brush and arrive at the cabin at dark.

But I was building up an energy debt. On the fourth night, after arriving at the cabin so bone-weary I barely had strength to eat dinner, I realized I wasn't as young as I once was. My body was having difficulty keeping pace with my spirit. I decided tomorrow would be a good day to kill a deer.

The sun was bleeding over the dark humps of mountains across the bay when I shoved my sore body out of the cabin the next morning. Clouds were forming over the sea and a stiff wind accompanied me upslope. I liked the idea of hunting with the breeze in Kodiak. There is no better wind sock than *ursus* nostrils, and after a showerless week, I figured no bear would want to be near me.

In less than three hours I'd passed through the brush zone, and was hiking the grass-covered spine between two bays.

I checked my rifle. Several of the bucks I'd watched the day before were mature three points. Sitka deer don't grow big racks by standards used to judge mule deer or Columbia black-tail. Ninety percent don't get beyond three points on each side. I wasn't after a Boone & Crockett trophy—I don't care about such things—but wanted a mature animal, one that I felt would aptly represent my hunt.

"For two weeks since I'd been boating around Kodiak, I'd watched deer through binoculars in that lustrous high country" (Gerry Ellis).

Two hours later I'd looked at ten mature bucks feeding on short tundra grass below me. Most had grown so fat on the lush summer grass that daylight was hard to find beneath their bellies.

In the early afternoon I began a side-hill approach to a grassy bench beneath a high point. When I reached the bench, two bucks jumped up, as startled as I was. We stood wide-eyed and stared at each other for long seconds until both deer bolted from the bench and began running across a draw toward a saddle in the main ridge. I hadn't studied the larger one at length, but the jumble of polished antlers convinced me he was the one I wanted to pack off the mountain.

As the two bucks filed toward the saddle I ran forward to the crest of the bench, threw my pack down, laid my rifle across it, and waited for them to crest the ridgeline. Kodiak returns no echo. Loud noises fade into the void of the high country and disappear. The crack of the rifle simply left and never came back.

I'd always heard Sitka black-tail are smaller than their southern relatives, but that wasn't the case with this 4 x 5 buck. Layered with fat and padded with nearly three inches of tallow, he was as heavy as any Columbian black-tail I've killed.

After reaching the buck I looked at the blue-emerald waters below. Except for the speck of the little cabin nestled near the bay, there was neither human sign nor sound. I followed a personal ritual of giving silent tribute to the life that had ended so that mine could continue. I also gave thanks to those who had the foresight to protect this land and to those who today, through vigilance and determination, continued to keep the road builders and developers at bay.

I paid the price for that wonder and solitude on the trip down the mountain that afternoon. But the 100 pound, three-hour pack was a bargain. And I'll continue to fork over that payment for as long as I'm able.

KARLUK KINGS

The following spring after the deer hunt, I found myself on Kodiak again. This time Tim Richardson and I teamed up for a backpack and king salmon fishing trip down the Karluk River on the southern end of Kodiak Island.

On the last night of our trip we were asleep in our tent next to the river when a noise awakened me. At first I thought I was dreaming. After opening my eyes in the darkness I was sure I heard snuffling and snorting.

It had to be a bear. The Karluk not only has the highest salmon numbers per lineal mile in Alaska, it seasonally has the highest brown bear densities in the world.

Flat on my back, I pulled a 44-magnum pistol from its holster beside my sleeping bag and laid the cold steel on my chest. Then I pressed the glow button on my watch and peered at the illuminated dial—4:30 a.m.

June darkness doesn't come to Kodiak until nearly midnight. Richardson and I had eaten fried salmon only five hours before. Even though we'd cooked and dined near the river away from camp, and cleaned up thoroughly, the big-nosed bruin must have smelled lingering evidence.

I stretched my eyelids in the darkness and tried to untangle the web of sleep hanging over me like a net.

Our trip began three days earlier, when we flew from Kodiak city to the village of Larsen Bay to meet Mike Carlson, owner of Larsen Bay Lodge. After tossing our backpacks into his Boston Whaler, Carlson whisked us up the bay. From there we followed a trail over a low mountain pass into the Karluk River valley below Karluk Lake.

Most folks float the Karluk with inflatable rafts delivered by float plane. But Richardson and I were after a different experience. Our plan was to backpack and fish down the river to the sea, where we would meet our return flight at the village of Karluk. We'd been hiking, fishing, and eating salmon for three days and were scheduled to reach the village that evening.

The Karluk is not a big river; a rock can be thrown across it anywhere along its 21-mile stretch to the sea. But in terms of salmon, however, it's enormous. In abundant years over 2.5 million humpies, sockeye, coho, dog, and king salmon leave the nutrient-rich waters of the Gulf of Alaska and surge up the river to the glacier-fed lake and surrounding spawning streams. In early June the river begins to swell with thousands of 20-to 40-pound, thick-bodied kings. These fat-laced salmon were the reason we were here. It's also the reason bears come to the river.

Suddenly I heard the heavy breathing again! I was awake now, alert and listening, every nerve in my body tingling. Where was the bear? Just outside the tent? Or in the brush thirty feet away?

"Bears are fundamental to the fabric of life on Kodiak"
(Howie Garber/wanderlustimages.com).

With my right hand gripping the pistol I used my left hand to silently grope for the flashlight while a tingle sprinted along my spine. I didn't have a plan. I wasn't sure what I would do with either the light or the pistol if a bear decided to share the tent with us.

There it was again! The snuffling, growling, snoring. SNORING!?

I switched on the flashlight and looked at Richardson. His breath caught with a snort and he inhaled in a series of growling, stuttered, snores.

I snorted in return, shoved the pistol back into the leather holster, and rolled over. But I was finished with sleep. The last of the stars winked from the slate-gray sky as I crawled from the tent and pulled on my boots. Soft pastels emerged against an awakening blue horizon as I walked to the edge of the river and sat on the grassy bank.

The Karluk begins its seaward journey beneath the snow-capped peaks of its namesake lake, exiting in a graceful series of braided oxbows through tundra ridges covered with dense brush and tall grass. Halfway to the ocean, the meandering stream bears its teeth and cuts a tight blue path through a range of treeless coastal mountains.

The first day with hazy green mountains beckoning in the distance Richardson and I cut across the oxbows and plowed through hillsides of alder brush and storms of mosquitoes and black flies. We camped on the river that night, but didn't start fishing until the following morning after we'd reached the mountains.

"Let's pull a spinner through there," I said, indicating a dark swirl of water and boulders between two canyon walls. Walking out on a gravel spit under a cobalt sky, we struggled from our packs and tied large, nickel spinners to twenty-pound test line threaded through eight-and-a-half-foot spinning rods.

I cast upstream and bumped the lure along the rocky bottom with the current. Suddenly it hung tight. I jerked upward. Nothing moved. Again I yanked on the rod. . .nothing. I pulled back hard, bending the rod nearly double. Suddenly the "rock" surged upstream and rolled with a golden boil in thick blue current.

Alaska's chinook salmon are called kings, because in the world of salmon, that's what they are. They are sovereign. When hooked in a river that rushes to the sea without rest, they couple their thick-slabbed sides to swift current with unquestionable authority. From a riverbank perspective, once a king is hooked, an angler's tranquil world is instantly converted to disarray. Subtle techniques like pin-point casting and measured retrieves are reduced to a marathon of staggering across wet rocks, sliding down muddy banks, and plunging through stream-side brush.

The blue monofilament line melted from my spinning reel as the salmon surged downstream. After a quarter-mile run with me in tow, it changed its mind, powered to the opposite side of the river, and bulled back upstream.

"Back so soon?" Richardson said, grinning as he leaned into his own duel with a king salmon.

Half an hour later neither of us had gained noticeable ground.

I watched Richardson as he braced his rod against his waist, switched hands and shook a cramp out of his right arm.

He had called in late winter to suggest we fish the Karluk River in early June for king salmon.

"We'll backpack down the river," he said.

"Do many people do that?"

"People float it in rafts," he said. "I've never heard of anyone who has backpacked it."

I should have recognized the voice of armchair-optimism.

Suddenly my thoughts were interrupted as Richardson's voice cut through the warm morning air. "Look!" Standing in knee-deep water he pointed to the mountain slope across the river.

Showing no interest that we were catching its winter food supply, a large Kodiak brown bear ambled across a grassy hillside while overhead two bald eagles rode canyon thermals.

It was a classic Kodiak scene, but I didn't have time to be mesmerized by it. I felt the salmon weaken. Pulling the fish closer, I knelt in the water and wrapped my hands around my first Kodiak king salmon.

Karluk kings are tied to a past older than mastodons and mammoths. The southern end of Kodiak Island, known as the Refugium, was spared the scouring effects of the Ice Age glaciers. This lack of genetic interruption is suspected of connecting these fish to a lineage over 80,000 years old.

I held the speckled, streamlined body evolved for slicing through oceans and rivers and thought about that ancient connection. With one hand wrapped around the thick tail and the other gripping its massive girth, I watched the leaf-like gill plates pump cold, oxygen-rich water and felt my own connection re-emerge.

Raised on the banks of a coastal river in Oregon, my life was once measured by the seasons of chinook, coho, and steelhead. But here, three thousand miles from home, I felt like an outsider searching for a vanishing richness I had known, but forgotten.

The great runs of fish that once surged into the rivers of the northwest are gone. Crushed beneath the relentless weight of industry and humanity, the wild salmon in Oregon's once-rich coastal rivers are hovering at one percent of their historic abundance. The sixteen million wild salmon that once filled the 2,500 watersheds and 266,000 miles of spawning streams in the Columbia River Basin have dwindled to a few thousand fish.

Why such a difference? Why, in a mere 150 years, has a species so critical to the web of life on the west coast remained abundant in one region, and reached the edge of extinction in another?

Is it overharvest?

Neither region has escaped a history of human plunder. One of the biggest salmon canneries in Alaska was built at the mouth of the Karluk River during the cannery boom in the late 1800s. For decades tens of millions of salmon were hauled from dams, weirs, traps, and nets that stretched across the slender girths of nearly all the Kodiak Rivers.

Finally, in the 1930s, laws were passed ending the unrestricted harvest, both in Alaska and Oregon. But half a century later, while the gravelled streams of Kodiak Island are once again annually carpeted with fish, salmon numbers have steadily declined in the northwest rivers to the south.

Are seals and sea lions eating too many salmon? That's a tempting answer, but it doesn't hold up to close inspection. More sea mammals lived on the Pacific coast in the early 1800s than are present today. And Kodiak salmon are currently exposed to as many sea and land predators as any salmon fishery in the world.

Is the demise of northwest salmon just a ruse, another example of environmental overkill? If the public is being duped, somebody's doing a whale of a job. In 1991 the American Fisheries Society published the results of a landmark study entitled: "Pacific Salmon at the Crossroads: Stocks At Risk From California, Oregon, Washington, and Idaho." The report identified 214 salmon stocks, of which 101 were at a high risk of extinction, 58 at moderate risk, and 54 of special concern. At least 106 major stocks of salmon had already gone extinct in the region.

There hasn't been a commercial or sport fishing season for coho salmon on the west coast since 1993. As this is written the only Oregon wild stocks of coho and steelhead that aren't listed for protection under the federal Endangered Species Act have been placed under state care to salve political friction over federal intervention.

Many point to changing ocean conditions as a primary factor in salmon production. And it's true. As a matter of fact it's always been true. For thousands of years salmon numbers have remained healthy during the ups and downs of ocean conditions. Only in the last few decades have Northwest salmon been so perilously balanced on the edge of oblivion. The reasons are tangled in a complex web of environmental alterations caused by a century of myopia towards nature and ecosystems, coupled with a century and a half of human meddling in the world of salmon, from dam building to artificial propagation to altering food chains in the ocean.

But as I held that powerful bolt of muscle in liquid ice beneath the untouched, glacier-carved mountains that towered above the Karluk River, I knew I was looking at a primary reason.

Coho salmon (Marion Owen).

No plowed fields or paved cities sprawl across the landscape. There are no channeled estuaries, no cattle-hammered riparian areas, no pesticide-laced streams, no headwalls scarred with roads or mines, and no mountains of timber to strip. Kodiak contains wild rivers flowing through a land changed little except through the measured pace of evolution.

As I knelt in the Karluk that day, I realized how sterile and disjointed our southern rivers have become. After a century of human development all we've left to salmon are crippled promises of technology and political rhetoric.

But there is no need for false optimism or imagination on the Karluk River, where multitudes of salmon still struggle upstream to waiting bears, birds, and even a few humans.

The salmon I held was solidly rooted to one place—one river. Following unknown charts through thousands of miles of ocean, it was irresistibly drawn back to the mountains of its birth to mate, die, and return its body to a timeless cycle. I sensed my own body strengthen as I held it.

Even as I felt the struggle return to its blood I didn't want to let it go. Finally, as I watched it slip from my fingers back into the blue depths, I felt an almost umbilical detachment.

Kodiak Island has more adult salmon return per lineal stream mile then any other place on earth. The Karluk was pregnant with fish. We caught more salmon, but catch-and-release fishing, as necessary as it might be, quickly lost its luster as we followed the river through the wild heart of Kodiak. Tiring fish to exhaustion simply for personal pleasure seemed no more than a narcissistic extension of our history with them.

Finally, haunted by that first touch, we decided to catch only what we could eat.

That last morning as I sat outside the tent and watched the sunlight climb down from the mountains and ignite the blue water, I knew why I had come here to touch and eat salmon. Every living thing on the island and in the water surrounding it are connected to the endless circle of salmon. My presence here had brought me once again into that circle. Kodiak had done something for me that Oregon could no longer do. It had brought me home.

Brown bears not only follow the same trails to the salmon rivers year after year, they literally step in their ancestors' footsteps.

It was a warm August morning in 1996 and I was on Kodiak again— this time on Olga Bay at the mouth of the Akalura River. I had wandered down to the water's edge with a breakfast plate of fried coho salmon. It was a good place to think. And it was a good place to enjoy breakfast. I flaked off a piece of the succulent orange meat from my plate and looked out at the bay.

Usually the huge North Pacific tides keep the water moving, but there is a window of calm as the tide reverses itself. This was one of those times.

It was my last morning on Kodiak for the summer. I was returning home to Oregon. A week earlier a friend and photographer, George Mobley, and I had flown to Akhiok, a village on the southern tip of Kodiak. Mitch Simenonoff, a native guide, met us at the airstrip. He piloted us north through the Olga Bay Narrows to an old salmon cannery at the mouth of the Akalura River. Constructed in 1892, the Olga Bay cannery, now a ramshackle complex of old buildings, was abandoned in the 1930s and operated as a base camp for bear hunters until the late 1980s. Akhiok Kaguyak, Inc., the local native corporation, now owns the old cannery and Mitch maintains one of the buildings for hunters, anglers, kayakers, and bear viewers.

George and I had come here to photograph bears. Mitch would boat us each day a few miles across the rough Olga Bay waters from the cannery to the mouth of Dog Salmon Creek where bears were eating salmon.

In late summer and fall, when salmon pack the rivers, brown bears follow the trails down from the high country before winter hibernation to pad their ribs with a thick layer of fat from a high-protein salmon diet.

I munched my breakfast that last morning and thought about the week spent photographing bears. Of all the earth's interwoven wonders that I've witnessed in the natural world from ancient trees and their importance to streams on the Oregon coast to the migrations of mule deer and elk in the Rocky Mountains, the connection of territory, space, and another species—in this case salmon—extends far more visibly to Kodiak brown bears than any other creature.

"A big sow with three cubs ambled down to the river" (Victor G. Barnes, Jr.).

Dog Salmon Creek, a shallow stream not more than 100 feet wide, flows only a few miles from Frazier Lake into Olga Bay. The bears know it well. The first afternoon we arrived, Mobley and I set up cameras, tripods, and big lenses on a bank covered with tall grass and willow, about a half-mile inland from the bay where the river shallows.

We didn't have long to wait. A big sow with three cubs ambled down to the salmon-stuffed river as the sun sank in the west. Her large three-year-old cubs splashed around and snagged a few tired fish, but mama was an old hand at the fishing site. Like any experienced angler she searched purposefully for coho fresh from the ocean. When she spotted a salt-spangled specimen among the hundreds of older and darker fish in the water around her, she chased only that chosen one. Once the prize was firmly clenched in her jaws, she dragged it to shore, where the entire family gathered in a growling, flesh-ripping feast that scattered pieces of fish like fertilizer.

Other bear families fish the river, with each staking out its own sites. Adults are acutely aware of territorial boundaries. Our human presence was no different. An unmarked line was drawn in the river about twenty feet in front of us. At times a bear would venture near it and eye contact was made. At that moment there was an unmistakable bear-to-human message: "You keep your distance and I'll keep mine."

The first time the big sow approached the line, I lifted my eyes over the camera lens and for an instant we stared into each others' souls. The unspoken communication was crystalline. It reminded me of my third grade teacher when my body language betrayed bad intentions. The look she gave said: "I'm watching you. Don't push it."

The look I gave in return said: "Yes, Ma'am."

An overpowering interaction of life dominates the river. A rushing sound from the steady movement of thousands of spawning salmon is a constant background. Males, their humped backs jutting out of the shallow water, rush others in a never-ending territorial defense. There is no time to fear predators, no urge to eat, no rest or energy conservation. Not even a delineation of day or night divides the procreation frenzy of salmon. Their world, in this last rush of life, has been reduced from the vastness of ocean to a square yard of glacial river gravel and a mate. The constant movement, competition, and vitality is an avalanche of life's completion.

The totality of this sparkling ecosystem is so visual it hits like a fist. There are no missing links or voids here. The circle is complete. The land's largest carnivores prepare for winter eating salmon bursting with ocean richness. White-headed eagles and jet-black ravens wheel among hundreds of seagulls and shorebirds, all picking at thousands of bits of salmon floating in the water and scattered on shore. Insects swarm on the leftovers, around the blood-smeared faces of bears and on every exposed piece of skin. Clouds of mosquitoes rise above the high, lush aquatic growth. Bats zoom through the haze.

Life here, in this vital junction between land and sea, revolves around the living and dying link of salmon. And in turn, the young fish thrive on the unbroken natural chain, spending their first year feeding on insects and sharpening muscles and survival skills against a host of predators, preparing for years at sea after which they return as finely honed adults and complete the circle, time and again.

During my time on Kodiak I've thought much about my presence in this circle, and how it has shaped and altered not only my life, but the lives of other non-human creatures I touch.

Granted, the change I cause is imperceptible, but it exists. The natural process of life is its own guide. Evolution is shaped by change. And it works—when life is balanced in the equilibrium of time and space. But we've tilted much of our world out of that balance.

We change the world fast today, probably too fast. We block rivers with concrete, alter their flow and temperatures and suck the water from them before we even understand how a salmon finds its way home. We alter migratory routes, forage patterns, and the structure of wildlife populations before we know how vital a thousand-year pattern can be.

There is a social struggle going on in America today over these changes. And that struggle is highly visible between current conflicts between hunting and viewing Alaska's grizzly bears. Bear viewing and photography, by nature, tends to habituate bears to the presence of people. Hunting, by nature, tends to have the opposite effect. Where the conflict is most intense, polarization is occurring over which human use should get priority on public lands.

Bears on Kodiak have been hunted by humans for their hides and red meat for at least 7,000 years. The first known reference to Kodiak as a "recreational hunting" destination was in 1899, when the Edward Harriman (the railroad tycoon) Expedition, touring coastal Alaska, stopped in Kodiak so Harriman could "shoot a Kodiak brown bear" to win a bet from a Chicago banker.

Throughout this century, hunting Kodiak's giant bears has been considered by many as a top big-game experience. The three biggest brown bears ever killed were taken from Kodiak Island. Of the top fifty bears in the Boone & Crockett records, thirty-three were taken from Kodiak.

Though the brown bear is still considered a pinnacle of the North American hunting experience—approximately 160 bears have been taken by hunters annually since 1980 on the Kodiak Archipelago through a strictly-controlled process—the tide of public desire is changing.

A four-year study of public use trends during the 1990s on Kodiak National Wildlife Refuge reveals participation in wildlife viewing rising by an astounding 259 percent, while sport hunting during the same time period declined by 14 percent.

Although these statistics demonstrate the greater demand for shooting bears with cameras over rifles and bows, they don't address the needs of the bears.

Existing bear research demonstrates the need of big bears for ample space apart from humans. And the brown bears of Kodiak who have traveled the same path for generations to fish the same streams are especially vulnerable.

Thousands of Gortex-clad urbanites freshly air-dropped only hours from high-rise, condo America with Nikon's latest technology dangling from their necks aren't any more conducive to a wild Kodiak ecosystem than quantities of modern day Harrimans who care more about impressing bankers in Chicago than they do about bears.

Both viewing and hunting can change the behavior of bears. The time I spent photographing bears in Olga Bay didn't directly kill any bears, but it had an effect. By sharing a corner of their river with me, it influenced the bear's (especially youngster's) behavior toward humans. The invisible "line" in the river disappeared after I left, but the bear's memory didn't. Those memories have the power to bring bears one step further from the wild. It may be a tiny step in the chain of evolution, but it's a step nonetheless.

Hunting kills individual bears but by both regulation and hunter preference, it is the large, older male bears that are taken most frequently by hunters. One effect of hunting the biggest males is that cub survival rates increase—fewer of them are killed by adult boars. Since the mature boars have had the opportunity to pass on their genes through several breeding seasons, regulated hunting poses no threat to the size of the animals. Indeed, the largest Kodiak bear that has ever lived could be roaming the archipelago today.

On that last morning on Kodiak Island I flaked off a chunk of the hot red flesh from the coho on my plate and tossed it into Olga Bay. A slender Mew Gull dipped down and snatched the piece of fish before winging back out over the calm bay.

The tidal transition was over, and as the water started moving again, schools of luminous adult salmon began passing through the shallow river's mouth. I stood holding my empty breakfast plate, watching the salmon return and understood why the bears on Kodiak have stepped in the same footprints to return to the same rivers for centuries.

If we can keep our human feet out of those footprints, the past can continue to be the future for Kodiak.

"All five species of Pacific salmon return to these icy waters" (Tim Richardson).

"The politics of Exxon Valdez *restoration came together not because habitat protection represented a 'land lock-up' to benefit bears at the expense of people, but because stakeholders had the patience and skills to fashion a result in which conservation and human use unlocked Kodiak's highest and best use for future generations."*

—*DOUGLAS H. GRANN*

 Public-private partnerships have become a key element in American conservation since the 1970s.

Even in Exxon Valdez *restoration, where the state of Alaska and the federal government had $1 billion to work with, private non-government organizations have played vital roles. Not only are these groups often able to act more quickly than governments in land acquisition or conservation easements, but the very fact that they do act provides political leverage for public officials to follow the private non-profits' lead with far larger financial resources.*

Raising funds for land acquisition, the Kodiak Brown Bear Trust and its partners have purchased small land parcels for donation to Kodiak NWR, augmenting lands purchased through the EVOS Trustee Council and through congressional appropriations for the Land and Water Conservation Fund. Among the Trust's partners are The Conservation Fund, Wildlife Forever, American Land Conservancy, Rocky Mountain Elk Foundation, Safari Club International, National Rifle Association, Camp Fire Conservation Fund, Vital Ground, Dallas Ecological Foundation, and the National Fish and Wildlife Foundation.

Wildlife Forever president Douglas H. Grann has ventured into remote areas of Kodiak and Afognak islands over the years. His perspectives offer a fitting conclusion to Kodiak Bears & the Exxon Valdez.

*Kodiak is home to Alaska's largest year-round bald eagle population
(Howie Garber/wanderlustimages.com).*

EPILOGUE

DOUGLAS H. GRANN

A century ago, naturalist John Burroughs found himself basking in gorgeous July weather on a hillside above the village of Kodiak. Below in the protected harbor of St. Paul rested the George W. Elder, an elegant steamer chartered by the Harriman Expedition of 1899. The voyage had begun in Seattle and toured coastal Alaska, stopping in Kodiak before continuing on to Plover Bay on Russia's Chukotsk Peninsula.

Railroad magnate Edward H. Harriman underwrote the expedition to determine whether a rail tunnel was feasible beneath the Bering Strait. He was taken with the breathtaking idea of a worldwide web of steel rails linking North America and the Eurasian land mass. He was also set on bagging a trophy Kodiak brown bear.

Harriman invited twenty-five of the leading scientists of the age and turned the two-month voyage into a floating university. The names of those aboard the expedition read like a pantheon of the American academy. In addition to Burroughs were geologist William Healy Dall, biologist C. Hart Merriam, forester Bernhard E. Fernow, landscape painter Frederick Dellenbaugh, photographer Edward S. Curtis, *Forest and Stream* publisher and Audubon Society founder George Bird Grinnell, who along with fellow voyager and Sierra Club founder John Muir shaped the early American conservation movement.

It was during their stop in Kodiak that an enraptured Burroughs gathered the impressions from which he penned the following depiction of Alaska's Emerald Isle:

"Kadiak (sic) I think won a place in the hearts of all of us. Our spirits probably touched their highest point here. . . .If we had other days that were epic, these days were lyric. To me they were certainly more exquisite and thrilling than any before or after. I feel as if I wanted to go back to

Kadiak, almost as if I could return there to live—so secluded, so remote, so peaceful; such a mingling of the domestic, the pastoral, the sylvan, with the wild and the rugged; such emerald heights, such flowery vales, such blue arms and recesses of the sea, and such a vast green solitude stretching away to the west, and to the north and to the south. Bewitching Kadiak! The spell of thy summer freshness and placidity is still upon me."

Anyone who has spent enough time on Kodiak to experience a similar patch of great weather can appreciate Burroughs' enthusiasm. The fact that the islands are in much of the same condition as in 1899 is a testament both to Kodiak's remote location, its lack of exploitable mineral or oil wealth, and the persistent public will over decades to safeguard this island of giant bears.

In fifty years, by 2050, the earth's human population is projected to rise from six billion to an astonishing ten billion. But if the remarkable conservation successes depicted in *Kodiak Bears & the Exxon Valdez* endure, Burroughs' tribute to Kodiak's charm will ring as true in the year 2050 as in 1899.

As someone who has been privileged to play a part in the habitat protection effort in the Kodiak Archipelago, I've often wondered about lessons that conservationists everywhere might draw from Kodiak.

At first glance it seems unlikely that Kodiak successes can serve as a model for conservation opportunities in less remote and spectacular locations.

How many multi-million acre swaths of roadless territory remain as pristine as the wild back country of Kodiak? How many places exist with an intact ecosystem that is home to as many brown bears as the habitat will support, and where abundant salmon runs are the norm?

How often do conservationists have the luxury of being able to work with a billion-dollar kitty resulting from a settlement agreement between government and one of the world's largest corporations?

How frequently can the political pieces be put together where all sides of an issue can achieve most of what they want?

These questions have persisted with me over the years because they argue forcefully against the notion that there are meaningful lessons from the *Exxon Valdez* habitat protection experience on Kodiak that can be applied to other conservation issues.

Much of Kodiak's topsoil is derived from volcanoes on the Alaska Peninsula. The aftermath of the 1912 Katmai eruption is shown here (Kodiak Historical Society).

After all, the nation has already protected many of its large, untouched spectacular landscapes: Yellowstone, Yosemite, Smokey Mountain, Boundary Waters, Olympic Peninsula and Glacier National Park. In Alaska, many of the best large landscapes were protected by the Alaska National Interest Lands Conservation Act of 1980 or by earlier federal conservation withdrawals prior to Alaskan statehood in 1959.

After the Grand Staircase Escalante National Monument was created in southern Utah in 1996, perhaps only the remaining million acres of unprotected roadless areas in the National Forest System and large blocs of roadless BLM lands qualify for conservation efforts on the grand scale of the *Valdez* restoration achievements.

But even if we've run out of Yellowstones, there is growing support in America to restore, enhance, and connect other relatively wild areas with each other, and to reverse habitat fragmentation by creating

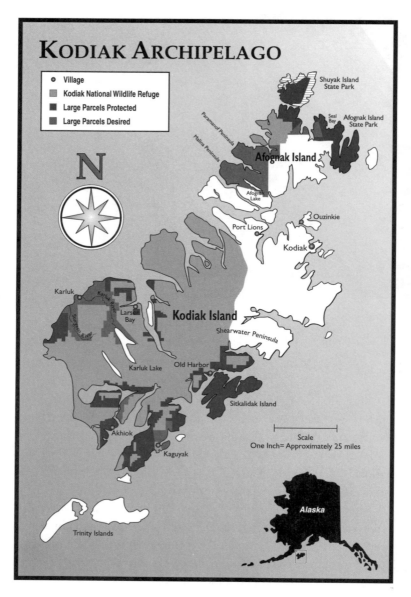

Kodiak archipelago protected lands and conservation targets (Eric Cline).

corridors for wild animals to move between protected areas and thereby mitigate or escape human-caused pressures.

For example, there were over 200 ballot measures in states and localities in the 1998 elections where voters could support open space and habitat protection initiatives. Seventy percent of them passed, even though all required new tax or bond revenue. "Smart growth" programs to combat suburban sprawl, protect farmland from development, enhance urban-park areas, and create greenways are proliferating across the country. There is obviously a vibrant constituency for protecting open space, wild country, and even the wild edges of tame country.

Add to this our growing knowledge of how to address the needs of fish and wildlife in the context of ecosystems instead of isolated species and there is cause for optimism. And while few places exist as untouched since the Ice Age as remote Kodiak, nature is enormously resilient. Even asphalt eventually surrenders to vegetation.

Although large populations of grizzly bears no longer exist in the Lower 48 states, committed people are hard at work preparing the conditions for the expansion of the grizzlies current range and their reintroduction to suitable habitat in the Intermountain West. America's black bear population is growing. Wolves, mountain lions, and some other predators are on the rise as part of a coordinated effort to restore as much of the nation's wildlife as possible to optimum population levels. "Rewilding" is an idea whose time has come.

Game species that were once endangered such as white-tailed deer, elk, wild turkey, wood ducks, and pronghorn antelope are thriving and in far better shape than in the days of John Burroughs and the Harriman Expedition. Waterfowl in general have enjoyed a remarkable resurgence. Conservation organizations have adeptly applied the science of wildlife management and habitat protection in success story after success story.

As for salmon, the picture is far bleaker, but at least the tide of extinction in the Pacific Northwest has captured the attention of the public and policymakers. Society is asking itself the right questions. The debate over issues such as water pollution, hydroelectric dam removal, unsustainable logging, and exploitative commercial fishing practices is raging. Public opinion surveys in the Pacific Northwest show broad support for enhancing salmon recovery even though the regional economy and individual citizens' pocketbooks will pay a price.

So yes, Kodiak habitat protection as part of *Exxon Valdez* restoration has occurred in an area of unique wilderness quality—with exceptional bear and salmon resources—but the successes on Kodiak also appear to be part of a national trend toward enhanced fish and wildlife conservation that is gaining momentum.

There are even strong parallels between the dollar amounts available in the *Exxon Valdez* restoration process and what leading political figures are calling for a decade after the oil spill. In 2000, the 106th Congress debated the Conservation and Reinvestment Act (CARA) designed to use federal outer continental shelf oil and gas royalties to sharply increase federal funds going into fish and wildlife habitat acquisition and conservation easements.

The Land and Water Conservation Fund (LWCF), enacted into law in the 1960s to direct off-shore oil revenues to habitat conservation, has been a sleepy, underfunded subaccount in the federal natural resources budget since the early 1980s. But its potential to protect critical wildlife habitat is capturing congressional attention as the nation's fiscal condition enters a period of budget surplus and external threats such as the Cold War are fading.

Proposals to fund the LWCF to the tune of $1 billion per year are being offered from both sides of the aisle and by the White House. These proposals mirror the successful open space ballot initiatives by state and local governments by attracting strong bi-partisan support even in an era where partisan animosity is the norm on Capitol Hill.

Passage of CARA or full funding for LWCF would represent at least the equivalent of a $1 billion *Exxon Valdez* settlement available for conservation every year.

So in the case of Kodiak viewed as an example of large-scale funding for habitat protection, it appears less of an exception than a harbinger of a trend in national political attitudes about the importance of healthy fish and wildlife habitat and open space. The EVOS Trustee Council's example of consensus building and power sharing between federal, state, and local interests is also indicative of a new and healthy trend in national conservation politics.

Conservation easements which guarantee Native subsistence rights are a key part of Kodiak and Afognak habitat agreements. Big Creek, near Old Harbor, shown here (Tim Richardson).

Lastly is the question of whether varying interest groups can successfully forge consensus in other conservation battles as they have on Kodiak.

Certainly one of the reasons habitat protection was popular with most stakeholders in the oil spill region is that the resource base is in such relatively healthy condition compared to most areas of the United States where conservation benefits are pitted against economic interests.

But here is where it is essential to understand what made the political consensus behind habitat protection come together in the Kodiak Archipelago. The point is that although Kodiak represents a remarkable wilderness setting, it is actually heavily relied on for economic purposes. And it is in understanding the risks and rewards that each party around the table faced in the *Exxon Valdez* habitat agreements that the applicability of the Kodiak model for other conservation is clearest.

From the landowner point of view the rewards of a deal were obvious.

Native corporations which owned land within the Kodiak NWR could receive tens of millions of dollars for keeping their home lands intact and undeveloped. The lands and resources would remain usable by villagers for subsistence hunting and fishing and managed by the State of Alaska and the U.S. Fish and Wildlife Service for sustained use. In this light, the *Valdez* agreements seem too good to be true.

On the downside, a small corporation suddenly becoming flush with cash with a shareholder base made up of people with low incomes and little experience handling large sums of money faces the danger of shareholder raids on those funds. This could lead to a dilemma of becoming a landless people with many shareholders having spent their money without a long term plan for the kind of economic self sufficiency Congress intended under ANCSA. Instead of the Native lands being there for all future generations, they would be sold and the cash proceeds of the sale spent by one generation. It would be hard to depict a worse outcome from *Exxon Valdez* restoration for the Native corporations. Conservation could win but indigenous people could lose big.

The solution the Native corporations devised was to retain substantial land holdings around their villages. Their retained land base assured that their 7,500 year link to ancestral lands would be preserved. The financial formula they adopted was threefold: to create permanent shareholder funds with some of the money so that money could last as long as the land; to dividend some money to this generation of shareholders to boost their well economic being; and to professionally invest the rest for corporate asset growth and further shareholder dividends.

Using this approach, the lands or conservation easements sold represented a normal corporate asset shift from real estate to financial securities. For a land rich, cash poor corporation, the habitat protection deals were perfect. Far from being an example of an uneconomic environmental result, the Native landowners unlocked the economic potential of their asset base and capitalized on one of the more exceptional stock market surges in U.S. history.

While some instances of dissident shareholder raids on corporate funds have occurred among Kodiak Native corporations, all the corporations have kept some form of permanent funds and all have kept a land base. The permanent fund and other corporate shareholder dividends have a benefit beyond the shareholders themselves because they annually spend money in the Kodiak and Alaskan economies thereby keeping some of the original oil spill dollars at work in perpetuity.

The state and federal land managers gained control of essential habitats, especially salmon rivers which form crucial food source links for bears, eagles, and other wildlife. The nightmarish scenario of having to manage complete ecosystems with control over only part of the habitat was ended by the *Exxon Valdez* habitat agreements.

The goal of the EVOS Trustee Council to restore oil spill injured fish and wildlife populations was made far more achievable by keeping critical nesting, feeding, and rearing habitats free of future disturbance by human development. The hope is that fish and wildlife utilizing the protected areas will flourish and repopulate the most heavily impacted areas of the oil spill region.

Habitat protection was an obvious win for the commercial salmon fleet, which forms the backbone of Kodiak's commercial fishery. Given the disappearance of viable salmon runs spreading north from California to British Columbia, the opportunity for Kodiak's salmon streams to be protected from development that could harm spawning systems was an unexpected biological windfall that will pay dividends for generations to come. Salmon face more threats than simply habitat loss, but if Kodiak's prodigious runs decline in the future it won't be because of degraded spawning and rearing areas.

Finally, the *Exxon Valdez* agreements forced Kodiak's recreation industry to make a choice. If they desired a "Lake Tahoe" development model for Kodiak's remote areas, then the habitat protection scenario would not be in their self interest. How could you subdivide the Native inholdings into hundreds of lodge and cabin sites if all the large private land blocs were placed in the Kodiak NWR or the Alaska State Park System?

However, the upside for existing remote lodges, back country guides, outfitters, air taxi, and boat charter companies is obvious. They have an operating region whose attractiveness will only increase as population growth places a premium on pristine remote areas. New companies based in the city of Kodiak or in the villages around the island can develop nature tourism to augment the already popular sport hunting and fishing uses.

Consensus building has been the hallmark of large-scale habitat protection in the Kodiak Archipaelago. Front row kneeling, left to right: Dan Sakura, Department of the Interior; Glenn Elison, U.S.F.W.S; Scott Stouder, Mule Deer Foundation; Tim Richardson, Kodiak Brown Bear Trust; Andy Christofferson, Marmot Bay Excursions. Standing left to right: Davey Panamarof; Ouzinkie Native Corporation; Howard Valley, Afognak Jount Venture; Ron Marcoux, Rocky Mountin Elk Foundation; Ole Olsen, Afognak Native Corporation; Glen Godfrey, Koniag, Inc.; Peter Olsen, Afognak Native Corporation; Pam Brodie, Alaska Rainforest Campaign; Jay Bellinger, Kodiak National Wildlife Refuge; Dave Cline, National Audubon Society; Jerry Sparrow, Blue Fox Bay Wilderness Lodge (Colleen Rankin).

In addition, the public access gained on formerly private Native lands has opened some of the best remote areas of the Kodiak NWR and on Afognak Island for outdoor recreation at its finest.

And so when the economic ramifications of the Kodiak habitat protection agreements are understood, the project should be viewed as far more than a win for bears, salmon, and wilderness. The *Exxon Valdez* Kodiak agreements are arguably the best economic investments for the region as well. Native corporation trust funds will continue being spent annually, salmon returns will remain strong and commercially viable, and wilderness based recreation will grow.

Of course there will be future challenges, including too much tourism pressure, but for the foreseeable future there is a harmony of interests between the bears, salmon, and humans. This, in the end, is the most important way in which Kodiak conservation can be viewed as a model for conservation success in less remote and spectacular areas.

And this lesson goes back a century to the friendly debate between Harriman Expedition members George Bird Grinnell and John Muir, over "conservation" versus "preservation."

The politics of *Exxon Valdez* restoration came together not because habitat protection represented a "land lock-up" to benefit bears at the expense of people, but because stakeholders had the patience and skill to fashion a result in which conservation and human use unlocked Kodiak's highest and best use for future generations.

The Kodiak success should be categorized as a victory for Grinnell's brand of conservation that sustains a remarkable wilderness-dependent species such as the Kodiak brown bear in a context of public and economic use. By contrast, as we enter the twenty-first century, the opportunities for Muir-style preservation are few—even when desired—and the more the advocates for wildlife grasp this, the greater will be our chances for success. That, in short, is the enduring legacy from the conservation success in the Kodiak Archipelago.

ADDENDUM

EXHIBIT I

EXECUTIVE ORDER 8857
Establishing the Kodiak National Wildlife Refuge
Alaska

By virtue of the authority vested in me by the act of June 25, 1910, c. 421, 36 Stat. 347, as amended by the act of August 24, 1912, c. 386, 37 Stat. 497, it is ordered that, for the purpose of protecting the natural feeding and breeding ranges of the brown bears and other wildlife on Uganik and Kodiak Islands, Alaska, without undue interference with the raising of cattle and other livestock thereon, both wildlife and livestock being of economic value to the inhabitants of the islands, all of the hereinafter-described areas of land and water of the United States lying on Uganik Island and on the western portion of Kodiak Island, Alaska, comprising 1,957,000 acres, more or less, be, and they are hereby, subject to valid existing rights, withdrawn and reserved for the use of the Department of the Interior and the Alaska Game Commission as a refuge and breeding ground for brown bears and other wildlife for carrying out the purposes of the Alaska Game Law of January 13, 1925, 43 Stat. 739, U.S.C., title 48, secs. 192–211, as amended:

The provisions of this order shall not prohibit or limit the hunting or taking of brown bears or other game animals or game birds or the trapping of fur animals in accordance with the provisions of the said Alaska Game Law, as amended, and as may be permitted by regulations of the Secretary of the Interior prescribed and issued pursuant thereto.

Nothing in this order shall be construed to preclude the exercise of, or to limit, the authority of the Secretary of the Interior under the provisions of section 2 of the act of May 1, 1936, c. 254, 49 Stat. 1250, or of other existing laws, to designate Indian reservations on the areas hereby reserved at such time or times it may become necessary or desirable to do so. The designation of any such Indian reservation by the Secretary of the Interior shall effect the removal of the lands included therein from the refuge established hereby.

This reservation shall be known as the Kodiak National Wildlife Refuge.

Franklin D. Roosevelt

The White House,
August 19, 1941

EXHIBIT 2

TERMS OF THE *EXXON VALDEZ* SETTLEMENT

Total $1 billion

Criminal Penalties
Fine for violation of provisions of Clean Water Act,
Migratory Bird Treaty Act and Rivers and
Harbors Act $150 million

    Paid: $25 million
               $12 million to North American
                   Wetlands Conservation Fund
               $13 million to Victims af Crime Act account
    Remitted: by the court due to Exxon's cooperation $25 million

Criminal restitution $100 million
    $50 million to state government
    $50 million to federal government

    Total paid for criminal liability $125 million

Civil Penalties
To state and federal governments over ten years $900 million
    for natural resource damages
(The largest dollar settlement of its type in United States history. The money goes
into a trust held in U.S. District Court. A state-federal Trustee Council decides how
the money is spent, then the court releases funds according to plan.)

Within 10 days of acceptance of settlement terms in 1991 $90 million
    December 1, 1992 $150 million
    September 1, 1993 $100 million
    September 1, 1994 $70 million
    September 1, 1995 $70 million
    September 1, 1996 $70 million
    September 1, 1997 $70 million
    September 1, 1998 $70 million
    September 1, 1999 $70 million
    September 1, 2000 $70 million
    September 1, 2001 $70 million

Source: *Exxon Valdez* Oil Spill Trustee Council

EXHIBIT 5

ORGANIZATIONAL STRUCTURE OF *EXXON VALDEZ* OIL SPILL TRUSTEE COUNCIL

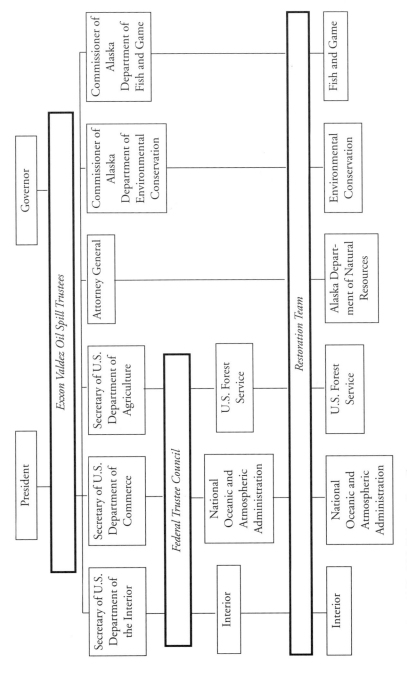

Source: *Exxon Valdez* Oil Spill Trustee Council

EXHIBIT 4

HABITAT PROTECTION AND ACQUISITION

Habitat Protection and Acquisition received the greatest share of public comment. Its place in the restoration program was discussed in almost every letter, brochure, and public meeting. It received overwhelming support as a part of the plan. The major disagreement about habitat protection was on emphasis: what should be emphasized and how much. In addition, hundreds of people recommended various areas for acquisition and protection—fifty areas in all.

Average allocation of the remaining settlement fund

	Origin of Response			
Restoration Category:	Spill Area	Other Alaska	Outside Alaska	All[1] Responses
Habitat Protection and Acquisition	60%	42%	81%	66%
Monitoring and Research	9%	12%	9%	9%
General Restoration	16%	19%	8%	16%
Administration and Public Information	5%	5%	5%	5%
Endowment (Including only those who *favored* endowment)	20%	40%	20%	20%

*The columns of the table do *not* total 100%. This is because the endowment allocations reflect the views of only those people who favored an endowment. In addition, 1,028 people provided an allocation to habitat protection and acquisition. Many of them did not specify how the rest of the fund should be allocated.

Source: *Exxon Valdez* Oil Spill Trustee Council

EXHIBIT 5

BIRD MORTALITY

Proportions (%) and total numbers of birds retrieved from Prince William Sound (PWS), Kenai Peninsula (KP), Barren Islands (BI), Kodiak (KOD), and the Alaska Peninsula (AP) between 25 March and 13 October, 1989.

Species group	Area					Total before 1 Aug[a]	Total after 1 Aug
	PWS	KP	BI	AP	KOD		
Loons	8.7	1.8	0.3	0.4	<0.1	1.5	<0.1
Grebes	11.8	1.6	0.2	0.3	0.1	1.7	<0.1
Procellariids	0.4	4.8	0.7	1.1	4.9	2.9	50.7
Cormorants	16.0	4.3	0.4	0.6	0.7	3.0	1.0
Sea ducks	24.9	8.4	0.7	1.6	0.7	5.3	0.3
Gulls	1.8	5.5	0.5	1.2	2.4	2.4	21.6
Murres	15.2	58.1	88.3	89.0	84.6	73.7	7.1
Murrelets[b]	11.6	4.9	3.7	0.6	0.5	2.2	2.0
Guillemots	4.7	4.6	1.2	1.6	0.8	2.2	0.4
Puffins	0.0	1.5	0.2	0.2	1.4	0.9	13.8
Other alcids	0.8	1.6	3.6	3.3	2.9	0.9	1.7
Other birds	4.1	2.9	0.7	0.1	0.9	1.7	1.3
Total numbers						2.5	
Retrieved	3,358	6,225	2,163	8,881	8,548	29,175	6,940
Identified	2,882	5,174	1,922	8,691	8,200	26,869	6,238

Source: *Exxon Valdez' Impact on Marine Birds*, Piatt et al.

[a] Includes 167 old carcasses that were oiled and apparently killed before 1 August, but retrieved after 1 August. Total does not include thirty-one oiled birds found on Middleton Island and 1,091 birds that died at oiled-bird rehabilitation centers.

[b] *Brachyramphus* murrelets only.

EXHIBIT 6

VALUE TO FISHERMAN
STATEWIDE SALMON

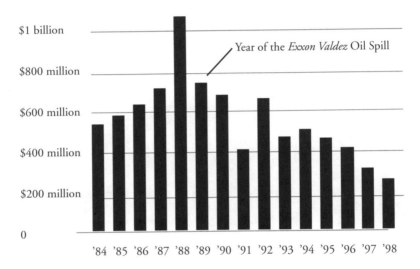

The yearly totals represented above have been adjusted for inflation. The U.S. Consumer Price Index was used to adjust historical earnings to relate the change in fishery earnings with typical consumer prices.

Source: Alaska Fisherman's JOURNAL January 1999.

Kodiak Bears & the Exxon Valdez

To Order Additional Copies of
Kodiak Bears & the Exxon Valdez
or to Learn How to Help
Kodiak's Brown Bears,

contact us at www.KBBT.org

Or write:

 KODIAK BROWN BEAR TRUST
1390 Buskin River Road
Kodiak, AK 99615

For Futher Information About
the *Exxon Valdez* Oil Spill

Write to:

EVOS Trustee Council
645 G Street, Suite 401
Anchorage, AK 99501

Or call:
907-278-8012

The EVOS Trustee Council can provide
additional information, books, and
research findings about all aspects of
the *Exxon Valdez* oil spill.

"What is man without the beasts? If all the beasts are gone, men would die from great loneliness of spirit, for whatever happens to the beasts also happens to man."

CHIEF SEATTLE